CLIMATE AND
ECONOMIC DEVELOPMENT
IN THE TROPICS

Climate and Economic Development in the Tropics

By DOUGLAS H. K. LEE

Published for the

COUNCIL ON FOREIGN RELATIONS

by

HARPER & BROTHERS

New York

1957

The Council on Foreign Relations is a non-profit institution devoted to the study of international aspects of American political, economic and strategic problems. It takes no stand, expressed or implied, on American policy.

The authors of books published under the auspices of the Council are responsible for their statements of fact and expressions of opinion. The Council is responsbile only for determining that they should be presented to the public.

CLIMATE AND ECONOMIC DEVELOPMENT IN THE TROPICS

Copyright, 1957, by Council on Foreign Relations, Inc.
Printed in the United States of America

All rights reserved, including right to reproduce
this book or any portion thereof in any form.

For information address Council on Foreign Relations,
58 East 68th Street, New York 21

FIRST EDITION

The Colonial Press Inc., Clinton, Mass.

Library of Congress catalog card number: LC 55-6586

FOREWORD

WHY is an underdeveloped country underdeveloped?

That is the question which prompted the studies which led to the writing of this book.

By any rational definition of "underdeveloped country" most of them lie entirely or partially in the tropics. Is climate the common factor that keeps them underdeveloped?

To be specific, why has the economic development of Brazil lagged behind that of the United States? Although both countries were settled by Europeans at about the same time, and although they both apparently have vast natural resources, and are about the same size, the United States has forged ahead economically. Why does one go ahead rapidly and the other at a much slower pace?

The same questions can be asked about other comparable countries where this factor of a hot tropical climate seems to be the common factor amongst the underdeveloped countries, and a temperate climate characteristic of the higher developed countries.

With the keen interest displayed of recent years in the problems of the underdeveloped countries it seems reasonable to try to assess once more the effect of hot climate on economic developments. Although much has been written on this subject many important questions are left unanswered. Much of the writing has been by what the author of this book calls the "cornucopia boys" who claim the tropical climate countries are the lands of the future, or by the pessimists, who rule out such countries as having no future whatever.

A few years ago I suggested that the question of the effects of hot climates on economic development should be studied by the Council on Foreign Relations. Over a considerable period of time I worked with Dr. Percy W. Bidwell, who was then the Council's Director of Studies, and with others, to explore the field and determine what needed to be done, how it might be accomplished, and whether the subject was suitable to the Council's interests and methods of work. After considering the results of this investigation, the Council's Committee on Studies authorized the work which has led to the publication of this book.

The reasoning that led to that decision, and some of the facts that helped determine the character of the study, are of interest. There was first of all the question why the Council, an organization concerned with United States foreign policy, should undertake a study that seemed to be largely in the province of medicine, the natural and applied sciences, and other fields where the Council had no special competence. The answer to this question lay at the heart of our study. The Council had an active interest in economic development. It had only recently concluded a major study of the interplay of social, political and economic factors in developing countries.[1] If climate had an important influence on agriculture, industry, and productivity, then it was most relevant to the further study of economic development. The United States government and private American organizations have been providing financial and technical assistance in the economic development of a number of countries. Perhaps its directions and emphasis, at least in certain places, would be different if the influences of climate were fully understood. The same might be true of private foreign investment.

So the problem became one of determining whether scientific research had produced a body of knowledge that could be used by laymen, so that economists, businessmen, and others concerned with economic development could take account of it in the guidance of governmental policy or privately-financed development projects. In our search we met some very interesting people and learned about a great deal of fascinating and significant work. But we did not find anyone who could turn over to us a document, or even a series of documents, and say, "Here is what we know."

This made it clear that the Council would have to start

[1] As a result of this study the Council published Eugene Staley's *The Future of Underdeveloped Countries* (New York, Harper, 1954).

one stage further back. Could it hope to fill this gap? We thought in terms of an inventory of knowledge. Bibliography seemed a logical starting place, but it was soon apparent that a comprehensive bibliography would require a staff of specialists working for a long time to produce a result that would be used only by other specialists. Valuable as such compilation would be, it was not the kind of work the Council could properly undertake.

Most of the specialists to whom we talked were sure that they and their colleagues had things to say that were relevant to our central questions. We thought so too after talking with them. They all emphasized a significant point: it was not only what they knew, but what they did not know that was relevant. Each could quickly name some problems in his own special field that had to be solved to make headway on the central question. They also agreed that the significance of some of the known facts was a matter on which the men of science had been known to have different opinions.

In this situation the Council opted for an exploration. It would bring together experts from many fields to explain the bearing of their knowledge and research on the problem of determining the influence of tropical climate on economic development. Without the precision of laboratory reports or the comprehensiveness of a massive bibliography, we would see if the exchange of views and the interplay of thought among men already steeped in the subject would give us a clear idea of what was known and whether it could be used to guide economic development. So in the fall of 1953 the Study Group on Climate and Economic Development in the Tropics was formed. Its members represented a great variety of skills and interests: geographers, climatologists, experts in soils and livestock, doctors, public health specialists, architects, engineers, businessmen, physiologists, economists, and men who had administered development policies and programs.

Our subject was a complicated one. Perhaps if we had all realized the complications at the outset, we might not have had the courage to start. Be that as it may. The Study Group did make the start, and the present volume is a result of its activities. The author, Dr. Douglas H. K. Lee, Professor of Physiological Climatology at Johns Hopkins University, acted as rapporteur for the group. An indefatigable worker, with a keen interest in this subject and a profound knowledge of it, he has drawn on his own research and experience, as well as on the group's discussions in preparing this book. He has produced a summary statement of what we know about the effect of tropical climate on agriculture, animal husbandry, human physiology and industry. He tells us what we have to do to use our knowledge more effectively. And he points to the places where more work needs to be done.

During our investigations it often seemed we had taken hold of a mighty "Who Done It." How to get the facts? We followed every possible clue as far as possible. Who is the villain in the underdevelopment of hot climate countries?

The reader will find answers to some of the questions about the effect of tropical climate on economic development. But, he will find we have raised many questions which cannot be answered reliably with present day knowledge. In some fields our knowledge is so meagre that trustworthy conclusions are impossible. In others the interpretation of the existing data is a matter of dispute—and that means more data are needed. There are many subjects which require more research. There is also need for coordination of knowledge about the complicated factors involved.

A tropical climate research organization is needed for continuous study of the direct and indirect effects of hot climates. It should be located in a tropical country. It could not only extend our knowledge of this subject but assist in the use of our present knowledge. Initially it should be concerned with co-ordination of existing knowledge.

Here in the United States some of our institutions of higher learning should establish chairs of, let us say, Human Ecology. By this means continuous study could be applied to the many factors involved.

Both of these ideas are worth the support of our great philanthropical organizations. Or so it seems to me.

As Chairman of the Study Group I want to express my thanks to those individuals on the staff of the Council on Foreign Relations who contributed so much to the activities of the group. And our thanks are also due to the many individuals who contributed so generously of their time and effort to make available the specialized knowledge which is the foundation of this book. The members of the group, the guests who led discussions, and the experts who attended our final conference, have all contributed substantially to this book.

The members of the Study Group were:

Heman Greenwood, *Chairman*
Douglas H. K. Lee, *Rapporteur*

Harwood S. Belding
Percy W. Bidwell
Jonathan B. Bingham
William Diebold, Jr.
James Terry Duce
William H. Forbes
Caryl P. Haskins
L. P. Herrington
Stephen B. Jones

Lester E. Klimm
Isador Lubin
Jacques May
Stacy May
Karl Pelzer
Oscar M. Ruebhausen
Paul B. Sears
Fred L. Soper
Charles Wagley

In addition to most members of the group, the following attended the final conference:

Marston Bates
Vining C. Dunlap
Frank P. Ellis
William A. Hance
Samuel P. Hayes
George E. Kimball
Robert C. Page

Robert L. Pendleton
Albert O. Rhoad
Anatole A. Solow
Frank N. Trager
Carl J. Wessell
Samuel H. Work

As a rule, discussion leaders were chosen from among the members of the group, but the following men participated in single meetings in that capacity:

J. G. Harrar
E. P. Palmatier
Ralph T. Walker

David Landman, a journalist, and Roger Ross of the Council on Foreign Relations, prepared the digests of our discussions.

The reader will conclude, I believe, that many ventures into economic development in the tropics should be classified more as speculations than investments. Also I think the reader will conclude that sustained research in the problems involved could remove many of the speculative features of such enterprises.

HEMAN GREENWOOD

Jacksonville
Vermont
October 1956

PREFACE

THE COUNCIL on Foreign Relations has long been aware of the political and economic problems that confront underdeveloped countries, and of the importance of the situation for the United States. It was led to institute an inquiry into the material conditions upon which the economic and social factors rest, by the process that Heman Greenwood has described in his Foreword. The Study Group on Climate and Economic Development in the Tropics organized by the Council was given the task of making a short-term estimate of present knowledge on this subject by getting together, at a short series of meetings, persons known to be well-informed on its different aspects.

Four evening meetings were held between January and April, 1954. These were followed in June by a three-day conference at which the ideas and conclusions put forward at the previous meetings were re-examined and consolidated. A number of specialists who had not attended the earlier meetings participated in the conference. Many of these men acted as discussion leaders when their specialities were being examined. Some prepared papers for the group's consideration. I have made use of all the group's records in writing this book, but without specific attribution save in a few cases where I have quoted remarks with the permission of their authors.

Heman Greenwood, who has travelled extensively in a life of international business, long ago became sceptical of the simple and categorical beliefs accepted by the public at large for half a century. As Chairman of the group he continued to exercise the insight and tenacity that had convinced the Council of the importance of this study. Without him there would have been no study group; without his chairmanship the group would have been far less successful in its task.

We had two major objectives. The first was to state the

present position of our knowledge concerning the effects of climate upon tropical development, so that policy makers, executives, and scholars could be reliably informed. The second was to indicate what further effort is needed to bring our knowledge to the pitch that sound practical guidance requires. In the process of reaching these objectives, we could be quite sure of defining what action could be taken, on the basis of present knowledge, to improve the situation.

Since the time spent by the group in actual study permitted little more than discussion of the main points, the preparation of a well-considered report by the group as a whole was not contemplated. It was decided to treat the discussions as a valuable exposition of the subject, with many of its ramifications and complexities, and to leave the preparation of a report to one person, who would exercise his judgment on the form, and accept major responsibility for the content.

As one whose activities have been largely devoted to the broad questions of man in the tropics, the author was glad to accept this assignment, not merely as an opportunity to put forward his own convictions, but also as a chance to hear the questions thrashed out by experts in various fields, many of them with wider experience than his own. The problem is one that cannot be solved from a knowledge of any one discipline, or from the content of any one person's experience. A diverse group of people, on the other hand, be they ever so cooperative, can hardly prepare an integrated document. The author believes that the method adopted here is one that is essential to the consideration of complex interdisciplinary problems.

If this attempt to bring into focus some of the scattered fragments of information stimulates efforts to find more significant pieces and to construct a more meaningful pattern, the work of the author and of all those who contributed to the discussions will have found its reward. If those succeeding efforts are in turn intimately linked to an active program for tropical development, it will have been repaid many fold.

D.H.K.L.

CONTENTS

TABLES

FIGURES

Chapter 1

BY WAY OF INTRODUCTION

ROUGHLY one-third the land area of the earth is in the tropic zone. About thirty per cent of the world's population lives there. Many of the countries, colonies, and islands that lie within or substantially within the geographic tropics (see Table 1) are commonly recognized as "underdeveloped"— a general opinion which a brief check of statistics will quickly substantiate. And there can be little doubt that the United States now occupies a critical position in relation to these less developed countries of the free world

With the decline of the colonial powers, the pattern of world trade has changed, so that the United States must now deal directly with tropical areas in both the purchase of raw materials and the sale of goods instead of through intermediary trading nations or in a circular pattern of international exchange. In the political sphere, the upsurge of nationalism has profoundly changed both the opportunity for and the mode of conducting intercourse with many of these countries. More than ever before the power lies in our hands for good or evil influence upon their peoples, their welfare, their attitude toward us, and ultimately on the success with which we all unite to preserve that which we find to be the good way of life.

In these countries there is generally a high incidence of disease, low inventiveness, and small use of mechanical power. There is also considerable unfamiliarity with the processes of democratic government or of self-government, where the countries have, until recently, been governed by an outside power.

The Study Defined

Logic demands that the purpose and scope of a discussion be clearly understood at the outset; therefore, definitions usually constitute the first order of business. The subject of

1

Table 1

COUNTRIES, ISLANDS, AND COLONIES IN THE TROPICS

A—Wholly within the tropics:

Guatemala	Angola
Honduras	Northern Rhodesia
British Honduras	Southern Rhodesia
El Salvador	Tanganyika
Nicaragua	Uganda
Costa Rica	Kenya
Panama	Somalia
	Ethiopia
Cuba	Sudan
Jamaica	British Somaliland
Haiti	French Somaliland
Dominican Republic	
Puerto Rico	Yemen
Virgin Islands	
Trinidad	Ceylon
French West Indies	Indo China (Laos, Cambodia,
Dutch West Indies	N. Viet Nam, S. Viet Nam)
British West Indies	Thailand
	Malaya
British Guiana	Singapore
Surinam	Indonesia
French Guiana	North Borneo
Venezuela	Sarawak
Colombia	New Guinea
Ecuador	Timor
Peru	Philippines
	New Caledonia
French West Africa	Fiji
French Equatorial Africa	Hawaiian Islands
Nigeria	Caroline Islands
Gold Coast	Solomon Islands
Ivory Coast	Mariana Islands
Liberia	Marshall Islands
Sierra Leone	Hong Kong
Portuguese Guinea	Macao
Belgian Congo	

B—Substantially within the tropics:

Mexico	Mozambique
Bolivia	Madagascar
Brazil	Mauritius
	South West Africa
Oman	
Saudi Arabia	Burma
	India
Bechuanaland	Taiwan

this book—the significance of climate for the economic development of the tropics—is easily recognized when held at arm's length but becomes blurred when examined at very close range. Indeed, any preliminary attempt to define the details will obscure rather than clarify the issue. Nevertheless, the reader is entitled to a general indication of the meaning of the terms used, although little more can be said in their defense than that they proved useful.

The term *tropics* as used here denotes those lands that have moderately high temperatures and high humidities throughout most of the year. *Economic development* inevitably provokes a question of standards. Does one really mean that New Guinea is underdeveloped as long as it abstains from the frenetic activity of New York? Or are the New Guinea natives to be permitted the choice of their own economic goals? If the latter, how can the "development" of New Guinea ever be compared with the "development" of New York? Inhabitants of technological countries readily assume that their way of life is to be desired by all—that "what is good for Nebraska is good for Nigeria." (The fact that even New Yorkers might dispute the meaning of "good" with Nebraskans is conveniently forgotten.)

Certainly, nearly everyone will agree that the average citizen of this country has "more" than the average inhabitant of India; but when asked to name the actual things in which we are more blessed, he finds some difficulty. Bathtubs? Yes! But are bathtubs so essential? Health? Yes! But health is hardly an economic commodity, although it may well be an index of economic status. Food? Decidedly, for here is something that comes close to being a universal index, although calories alone are not enough. Against all the material considerations, however, a Rousseau would pit moral satisfactions; and it would be a bold man, indeed, who would claim for any culture a clear superiority in such matters.

Because of uncertainties such as these, this book concerns itself with *the effects that climate may have upon any effort to increase the productivity of the regions characterized by moderately high temperatures and high humidities throughout most of the year.* The question whether an increase in productivity is desirable or not is thus avoided, since the problem to be studied is the effect of climate upon any increase which is actually attempted. The term *productivity,* in turn, is understood to cover those items which have value and are useful under the prevailing conditions, whether by local consumption or by exchange for imports. Nonmaterial products of human activity meet the terms of this definition if they contribute to cultural needs. In this sense, economic development is a movement toward the satisfaction of felt needs.

Behind this definition lies the conviction that social evolution is as inevitable as organic evolution; in other words, that the trend will always be toward the more highly organized structure which provides greater flexibility of action and more chance of stable operation under a wide variety of circumstances. In this process the smaller, less highly developed, or more remote countries will inevitably be involved. The move for integration may come either from the less developed countries desiring some of the material benefits of more complex cultures, or from the desire of the technological countries to ensure the supply of needed raw materials. Whatever the immediate cause, development will be attempted, increased productivity of some kind will be essayed, and contact and convergence of cultures will occur.

Perspectives

To the contemplative men of every age the conviction probably comes that theirs, above all others, sees the most critical developments in human progress. To us, the age of nuclear fission, antibiotics, jet propulsion, and synthetic fibers seems changing with a speed which can hardly be attributed to the mere rush of nearby scenery as we travel our particular portion of history. Be the facts of relative motion what they may, it is significant that not merely in material matters do we stand in the midst of critical transition. It is not too rash, for example, to consider that we are approaching some form of international intercourse which may make physical warfare unnecessary, however uncertainly and imperfectly the system may operate at first; or that "the material means of satisfying human desires" are yielding to a degree of understanding which may eliminate periods of world-wide economic disaster.

The specific problem of the role played by climate in the economic development of the tropics, rather than the generalities of internationalism or economics, is the subject of this book. Even in this restricted field, we seem today to stand in a privileged, and responsible, position. Until the sixteenth century the people of the tropical regions enjoyed what might be called the *period of isolation*. With the exception of small raids by contiguous groups, or the occasional and usually accidental intrusion of individuals from farther regions, the inhabitants of the tropics were largely undisturbed by developments elsewhere. Even those racial migrations which traversed some of the tropical areas worked but slowly to transform the lives of the indigenous peoples, and usually without any clear reference to the needs or desires of the areas whence the migrants came. The Southeast Asian region naturally experienced the greatest disturbance through relative ease of access, whereas the tropical sections of Africa were largely protected by the desert barrier, and those of Australia and the Americas by the oceans.

The sixteenth century saw the achievement of circumnavigation. The possibility of undertaking long sea voyages with a secure sense of direction and some assurance of return, consolidated by William Gilbert's theory of terrestrial magnetism, changed forever the relationship between the secluded places of the earth and the restless cauldron of modern civilization. Be he adventurer or explorer, a seafarer needs ships and equipment, and his crews need money. Financial support is forthcoming in quantity only when something can be expected in return. With grim inevitability the period of isolation gave way to the *period of exploitation*.

Although one should not assume the emotional attitude that every aspect of exploitation is reprehensible, one must admit that the central objective of tropical development by a temperate power was the profit of the developing power. There were many more humane colonizers and enlightened entrepreneurs than historical novels would have one believe; and the exploited countries also reaped enormous benefits in the way of improved health, expanded commerce, and public works. But these were necessary means to the winning of wealth or charitable dispensations by the more generous members of the dominating nation. The basic intent of this period is justly termed one of exploitation.

The birth and growth of this period were inevitable; equally inevitable were its decline and death. As with many another social and economic situation, two world wars may seem to have brought on the change; in reality they merely accelerated, or gave opportunity for, processes already in the making. Sooner or later exploited peoples covet the benefits of technology and the fruits of their labor for themselves. Sooner or later the opportunity comes for realizing their desires, especially as they acquire the technical knowledge necessary to continue development under their own direction. Today, in nearly all parts of the tropical world, we see the *period of self-development* succeeding that of exploitation. "Economic dynamism" is no longer a Western prerogative.

In the current scene the United States occupies a difficult but challenging position. On the one hand, our culture is a direct outgrowth—some would have it the culmination—of the European temperate civilization. We are driven by the same spirit, we seek the same goals of continuous progress, we need the same raw materials with which to fashion our products, and, while we may criticize our cousins roundly, we are proud of the heritage they have given us. On the other hand, we have by choice—often vigorously expressed—determined to stand aside from colonial expansion and exploitation, and we like to think of ourselves as genuinely altruistic in our offers of aid and assistance to the less privileged members of the family of nations. It is not easy to reconcile in practice the detailed demands of these two sets of motivations, nor is it easy to convince others that our decisions are indeed reached through clear and logical thinking.

This confusion of motivation has been worse confounded by marked divergence of opinion on the adaptability of the "white" man to tropical climates. To sailors and traders the dangers and drawbacks of the tropics were painfully, or fatally, obvious. Malaria and yellow fever, crocodiles and cobras, lay in wait for the unwary, while dysenteries and distempers continued to hamper the crews long after the visit. Even at home the "mysterious tropical disease" could carry off anyone who had been venturesome enough to brave the unknown terrors of the jungle. For those staying in the colonies, ever nostalgic for the homeland, the climatic discomforts remained clearly in the consciousness, constituting a topic around which petty frustrations and major derangements alike could be assembled. It was only natural that they should build up a coherent theory in which their role as overseers rather than executors of labor, the necessity of segregating their children from the indigenous populace, the desirability of frequent "leaves," and the unexplained bouts of physical indisposition were attributable to the baleful effects of the tropical climate on the white man.

This comfortable social theory of climatic influence received strong backing from the deterministic school of geographic writers, of whom Ellsworth Huntington of Yale was the acknowledged leader and prophet. At the time when these writers examined the problem, experimental data and physiological insight into the probable mechanisms of climatic action were almost entirely lacking. Practically the only method of study by which they could supplement limited personal experience was to seek correlations between climatic conditions on the one hand and human achievement on the other.

As an initial method of investigation this was perfectly justifiable; but the conclusions drawn from such studies can never be conclusive. In fact, it is dangerous to treat them as anything more than suggestive. The associations between events may be far different from what they seem: statistical theory may give the odds for and against occurrence by chance but cannot prove cause and effect; vital evidence may be missing from the assembled data; the things enumerated may not be at all what their nomenclature suggests. Above all, in the ever-changing patterns of human relationships, history does not necessarily repeat itself. What has been is not necessarily what had to be, let alone what has to be in the future.

As I have had occasion to remark elsewhere (21),[1] when Huntington commenced his work in 1907, the data he needed were not easily obtained, and those that were obtainable were often of doubtful quality. Inductive logic, the process of building generalizations from an accumulation of data, had received a tremendous fillip from Darwin's brilliant handling; but there was little guidance for those who possessed something less than Darwin's skill in its use. Physiologists and physicians, to whom Huntington might have turned for guidance in biological matters, were still preoccupied with other tasks or insufficiently advanced in tropical medicine to be of much assistance. It is perhaps understandable, though none the less regrettable, that from an isolated study of associations a full-blown gospel of climatic determinism rapidly emerged. Causal relationship was assumed where even association was doubtful; the great importance of culture apart from climate was often forgotten. Categorical statements were accepted as gospel: "The geographical distribution of health and energy depends on climate and weather more than on any other single factor. The well-known contrast between the energetic people of the most progressive parts of the temperate zone and the inert inhabitants of the tropics and even of the intermediate regions, such as Persia, is largely due to climate." (18)

So keen is man's interest in his own welfare, and so readable was some of the prose, that the writings had an immediate popular appeal—an appeal that is still evident. For the most part, readers were not in a position to know the limitations of either the evidence presented or the method of analysis. Many found in the deterministic doctrine a welcome weapon against the few who had the temerity to challenge the racial superiority of the European. A strong bond of sympathy existed between the preacher and the congregation—and there is nothing so easy or so successful as preaching to the converted.

But even in the heyday of geographic determinism there were dissenting voices. One group in particular felt that they had been somewhat maligned by the widespread belief in the inevitable degeneration of tropical man. These were the

[1] Numbers in parentheses refer to publications listed in the Bibliography.

almost wholly Caucasian and predominantly Anglo-Saxon inhabitants of tropical Australia. Their case was clearly summarized by Cilento in 1925 (7), but the form of publication, in a Health Department booklet, did not win for it the circulation and attention that it deserved.

In tropical Australia . . . there is practically no circumstance which can be laid hold of as representing a definite disability to the white race other than those faulty circumstances of social environment which are inseparable from the opening up of a new country for the purpose of primary production. First-generation, second-generation, and third-generation Queenslanders are performing their life work and following their ordinary avocations as they would in temperate climates, and there is at present no indication that the strain of tropical life is an actual one, or that the outlook for these people is anything but hopeful.

This was the burden of Cilento's plea; but few ears were then attuned to hear it. Grenfell Price, another Australian studying European colonization in the tropics, also sounded loud warnings against acceptance of environmental determinism but did not take such an extreme position as Cilento (37b).

As time went by a wave of reaction spread through geographic circles, until today the great preponderance of opinion is antideterministic. Unfortunately, some of those who could have led the way back antagonized their potential followers by too vigorous an attack upon the old without sufficient exposition of the new. As in most human affairs, it is not sufficient to be *against* something; one needs to convince one's listeners of the importance *of* something. Nor was the cause of rational consideration greatly helped by the *cornucopians*—those who represent the tropics as an inexhaustible storehouse of untold wealth. Mere assertive optimism is no real answer to deterministic pessimism.

In the midst of these uncertainties, the certainty of one thing has made itself increasingly apparent to those concerned with the best interests of the United States. Confusion there certainly is as to just how this country should conduct its foreign relations, and misunderstanding there certainly is as to the adaptability of the white man to tropical conditions; but there can be no doubt as to the critical position occupied by this country. From this position of responsibility and uncertainty this book proceeds to review the evidence on the role of climate in the economic development of the tropics. After a brief consideration of the nature of tropical climates, the role of climate will be examined in relation to crop production, animal husbandry, human health and efficiency, and industry. A final chapter will summarize the evidence and indicate the nature of action that should be taken, insofar as climatic effects are concerned, both in utilizing present knowledge and in pursuing new research to promote the economic welfare of tropical inhabitants and to enable our own country to play its role effectively and well.

Chapter 2

TROPICAL CLIMATES

THE WORD *tropics* basically refers to the area lying between the latitudes marking the "turning" of the sun and should, therefore, include all regions between the Tropics of Capricorn and Cancer. In accordance with a common practice, however, the term is restricted here to denote those lands which have moderately high temperatures and high humidities throughout most of the year.

In this narrower sense the term is largely synonymous with *equatorial lowlands;* but since political boundaries seldom coincide with climatic delineations, cognizance has to be taken of conditions which do not meet this definition. Areas with higher temperatures and lower humidities, for example, form part of the economic and political structure of countries like Mexico, India, and Nigeria. This necessity for retaining some flexibility of concept is increased by the fact, often overlooked, that within the tropics, even in the narrower sense of the word, there is considerable variation. Most people think of the islands from Sumatra to the Solomons as experiencing a uniform and typically "tropical" climate. The visitor is usually surprised to find that not only are there extensive mountainous areas, some with snow, but even on the coastal lowlands conditions vary noticeably from one place to another. On the eastern end of the main island of New Guinea, for example, Port Moresby, Lae, Finschaven, and Madang have distinctly different climatic regimes although all could be included in the term *lowland equatorial,* or *tropical.*

Before embarking on a discussion of the role played by climate in economic development of the tropics, therefore, it will be helpful to examine the nature and distribution of the varieties of tropical and near-tropical climate a little more carefully. At the same time it is advisable to anticipate

11

certain technical points by noting the manner in which the several climatic "elements" act upon plants, animals, man, and materials to produce the various effects that will come up for consideration in later chapters.

THE NATURE OF CLIMATE

Climate has often been referred to as the average condition of the weather. In many respects this is a useful definition since it emphasizes the habitual, as against the day-to-day variation in conditions. But it also tends to obscure the fact of variation, which may bear importantly upon certain climatic effects. To understand climate, moreover, something more than the mere collection of statistics that might be implied in the word "average" is required. Statistical data are essential, but they are only the raw materials upon which an understanding must feed. Such understanding can come only from the critical examination of the data; then, the formulation of tentative hypotheses to explain the observations; and finally, the testing of the hypotheses by re-examination of old data, collection of new data, and experimental inquiry in a continuing sequence until an adequate picture, as distinct from a mere collection of figures, emerges.

Elements and Factors

We are not concerned here with theories about the causes of climates. Since our interest is with the climatic conditions that exist and the effects they produce, a very brief statement of their origin will suffice to put the climates of the tropics in their proper setting.

Climate may be regarded as the combined behavior of certain climatic *elements:* namely, temperature, humidity, precipitation, air movement, radiative conditions, barometric pressure, ionization. These elements, or momentary conditions, derive from more constant climatic *factors,* or characteristics of the locality. Certain factors, such as latitude, altitude, distribution of land and water, contours, and soils, are fixed. Other factors, such as currents, winds, rainfall, drainage, and vegetation, are dependent and intermediate between the fixed factors and the elements.

The interaction of the factors determines the pattern displayed by the elements. But the elements in turn affect, to some extent, the dependent factors so that conditions tend to perpetuate themselves. Within the limits of the generally stable pattern, however, considerable fluctuations may occur, and conditions that are quite distinct from the mean may have to be taken into account. Exceptional deviations of this sort may be important where even a brief spell of unusual conditions could be critical to plant production, animal life, or human welfare. A short period of heavy rain may bring disastrous floods, or a few days of high temperature and humidity a high incidence of heat deaths.

The amount of heat received annually from the sun is greatest at a latitude of about 15° and is almost as great at the equator. Over the broad belt from 15° N to 15° S, therefore, conditions are likely to be hot throughout the year. The heat enables the air to hold a considerable amount of water vapor; the wide expanses of ocean provide this water vapor; low barometric pressure favors the landward movement of air; mountain ranges bring condensation and fill extensive river systems with water. Heat sets up a cycle of evaporation-thunderstorm-rain-evaporation in the mountains and watered plains, and the tropical climate is constantly being regenerated.

At higher latitudes the summers may be hotter, since a high intensity of solar radiation is then combined with a long summer day; but the winters are correspondingly cooler. Here, also, seasonal effects may be accentuated by wind changes, producing monsoons. The central portions of the large land masses at the higher latitudes, however, are likely to be relatively dry.

The Significance of the Elements

In studying the significance of tropical climates for problems of economic development, one could start with observed economic events such as a low productive level and try to trace out the climatic circumstances responsible for the observed state of affairs. This process of reasoning back from the events is, indeed, very common and usually constitutes a first approach to problems of this kind. It is open to so many fallacies, however, that conclusions drawn from this line of argument should be treated with considerable reservation unless they are clearly supported by other and preferably clearer evidence. The converse process of working out the possible effects of specific climatic factors, singly and in combination, while by no means free of fallacies, usually provides better information in the long run. It is the procedure that will receive the greater emphasis in the pages that follow.

At this point it is necessary to list the major direct effects that various climatic elements may have upon man and the things which he depends upon for his welfare; namely, soils, plants, animals, and materials. The more important direct effects, as set out in Table 2, are numerous, varied, and pervasive. When the probability of interaction among the broad categories—soils, plants, man, animals, and materials—as well as the interaction among items within the categories is taken into account, the scope for climatic effect becomes vast. Thus, the questions that will arise in each subsequent chapter are not so much whether climate can have an effect, as the extent of its effects, the possibility of counteracting them, and the net significance for economic development.

CLIMATIC CLASSIFICATION

Infinite variety is possible in the details of climate. Even though certain types may be picked out, insensible transitions will occur between one type and another. Nevertheless, many of man's activities call for a working classification, if only to indicate the general conditions likely to be found in different areas. For practical purposes, the infinite variety is divided into a limited number of classes; but both the classifier and the user must be fully aware of the limitations of any such breakdown. Wherever a dividing line is put, somebody will want it moved north, someone else will want it moved south. If a temperature of 86° is taken as a dividing point, somebody will ask why 85° or 90° was not used. Furthermore, the data upon which the classifications are based are not entirely reliable. At best they represent conditions at the precise place of the observing stations, and these have an extraordinary variety—the tops of buildings, city streets, airports several miles from the city of the same name, irri-

Table 2

ACTION OF CLIMATIC ELEMENTS

Action upon

Element	Soils	Plants	Man and Animals	Materials
Temperature	Favors breakdown of organic materials. Increases solution of minerals and nitrogenous substances.	Favors growth and maturation. Increases water loss and tendency to drying.	Interferes with heat loss.	Favors breakdown. Increases drying. Softens plastics.
Humidity	Retards drying. Favors breakdown of organic material. Promotes micro-organisms. Favors solution.	Favors growth. Restricts water loss.	Interferes with heat loss. Favors some skin disturbances. Causes some discomfort to man.	Increases water content. Favors micro-organisms. Favors oxidation.
Wind	Erodes exposed ground. Deposits dust in other areas. Favors drying.	Increases water loss and tendency to drying. Aids pollination and seeding. May do physical damage	Favors heat loss unless very hot and dry. Sometimes annoying.	Favors drying. Adds to mechanical effect of rain and dust. May cause mechanical damage.
Solar radiation	Raises temperature of surface (see above).	Governs photosynthesis. Raises leaf temperature (see above).	May give sunburn. Raises surface temperature (see above).	Often specific cause of breakdown. Raises temperature (see above).
Rain	Erodes and leaches. Produces packing of clays.	Essential for supply of water. May do physical damage.	Substitutes for sweat. Sometimes annoying. May produce flood danger.	Greatly increases water content. Promotes solution. May cause mechanical damage.
Dust	May be deposited.	May do physical damage.	May give physical annoyance.	May do physical damage.

gated patches of desert, or bare rocky outcrops. Most published data deal with mean or average values, the limitations of which have already been mentioned.

If one were concerned with indicating the origins of climate, it might be possible to think of a single, comprehensive classification; but when one seeks a classification suitable for practical problems, the number of possible classifications becomes almost as great as that of the problems. Even though the same climatic elements may be concerned, their relative significance, or the method in which they should be expressed, is likely to vary with the problem. Classifications which are eminently suitable for discussing the effect of climate on plant growth may be virtually usless for indicating the direct effect on animals or the effect on human disease. In view of the number of different problems encountered in considering the effect of climate on economic development, one cannot expect to find any single classification adequate to all purposes. Some of the more useful classifications will be briefly set forth here to illustrate the inevitable diversity, as well as to show what procedures are available.

Köppen Classification

The best known and most generally used classification is that developed by Köppen (23) to the form in which it finally appeared in 1936. Köppen was faced with the necessity of providing a classification which would be sufficiently detailed to make valid differentiations between patterns and, at the same time, sufficiently simple to be grasped by the practical man. He was also hindered by the fact that adequate data existed only for temperature and precipitation. For our purposes it will suffice to note that Köppen defined eleven climatic types, with a code for further subdivision where necessary. The principal types and the code for subdivision are given in Table 3.

Such a classification is strictly pragmatic. Although the supposed effects upon man are mentioned, the criteria used for delimiting the classes are frankly botanical in many cases. In accordance with the demands of science for quantitative and logical procedure, attempts have been made to devise a more satisfactory division of climatic patterns. Greathouse

Table 3

KÖPPEN'S CLASSIFICATION OF CLIMATES (23)

Principal climatic types

Af   tropical rainy climate
Aw   tropical savanna climate
BS   semiarid (steppe) climate
BW   arid (desert) climate
Cf   warm temperate rainy climate without dry season
Cw   warm temperate rainy climate with dry winter
Cs   warm temperate rainy climate with dry summer
Df   cold snow-forest climate without dry season
Dw   cold snow-forest climate with dry winter
ET   tundra climate
EF   frost or icecap climate

Subdivision code

a ⎫
b ⎬ in C or D climate { with hot summer
c ⎭   with warm summer
                          with cool, short summer
d   in D climate   with very cold winter
H   polar climate due to high altitude
h   hot, dry climate
I   small annual temperature range
k   cool, dry climate
k′   cold, dry climate
m   mixed or monsoon type of tropical climate
n   dry climate with frequent fog
n′   dry climate with high humidity

and Wessell (16) found, however, that a simplified version of the Köppen classification is useful for considerations of deterioration in materials, and a summarized description will be found in their text.

Thornthwaite Classification

In his first classification (47b) Thornthwaite used vegetation as a means of determining climatic boundaries. In a later presentation (47a) he proposed certain climatic criteria, but they are of such a nature that they apply primarily to botanical needs:

Moisture Index—This is a comparison between the net water surplus or deficiency on the one hand, and water need on the other. Both items involve a quantity defined as *potential evapo-transpiration,* which is the water that would be evaporated directly or through transpiration from an area if it were available. (It is thus to be differentiated from actual evapo-transpiration.) The computation, a complex one, is given in part in Thornthwaite's paper. By means of the Moisture Index climates may be classified as follows:

A	Perhumid
B_4	Humid
B_3	Humid
B_2	Humid
B_1	Humid
C_1	Moist subhumid
D	Semiarid
E	Arid

Seasonal Variation of Effective Moisture—By considering the seasonal distribution of the data making up the Moisture Index, a second subdivision can be prepared as follows:

Moist Climates (A, B, C)		Dry Climates (C, D, E)	
r	little or no water deficiency	d	little or no water surplus
s	moderate summer water deficiency	s	moderate winter water surplus
w	moderate winter water deficiency	w	moderate summer water surplus
s_2	large summer water deficiency	s_2	large winter water surplus
w_2	large winter water deficiency	w_2	large summer water surplus

Index of Thermal Efficiency—This is simply potential evapo-transpiration, which is used as a means of classifying climates according to their warmth, on the grounds that both depend upon day length as well as temperature. The subdivisions and their symbols according to this criterion are:

A'	Megathermal
B'$_4$	Mesothermal
B'$_3$	Mesothermal
B'$_2$	Mesothermal
B'$_1$	Mesothermal
C'$_2$	Microthermal
C'$_1$	Microthermal
D'	Tundra
E'	Frost

Summer Concentration of Thermal Efficiency—In general, as we pass from the equator to the pole the evapo-transpiration will tend to become more and more concentrated in the summer months. There are certain irregularities in this process, however, so that a fourth classification is advisable. According to the summer concentration of evapo-transpiration, climates are classified as follows:

48.0% and less	a'
48.1 - 51.9	b'$_4$
52.0 - 56.3	b'$_3$
56.4 - 61.6	b'$_2$
61.7 - 68.0	b'$_1$
68.1 - 76.3	c'$_2$
76.4 - 88.0	c'$_1$
Over 88.0	d'

A given climate is denoted by the appropriate symbol from each of the four classifications. Thus Seattle, Washington, is B$_2$ B'$_1$ s a' and Los Angeles, California, D B'$_2$ d a'.

The Thornthwaite system has been applied to several regions for which the necessary data have become available, but a wide coverage is not possible until better information is at hand. Up to now it has been found to apply fairly well to plant requirements, but anything finer than the major subdivisions does not accord well with direct climatic significance for man.

Physiological Classification

Since the classifications that are satisfactory for plant problems prove unsatisfactory for human and animal problems, more suitable schemes for the latter need to be devised. For various reasons that the author has discussed elsewhere (21) physiologists have preferred, however, to seek some one index of the combined effect that climatic elements have upon man and to postpone serious consideration of classifying climates until that index is available. How far they have progressed with their search will be discussed in Chapter 5; for the present they have been content to regard any classification as of strictly limited and interim value.

Special Classifications

Numerous classifications have been made for special and limited purposes, giving consideration only to those climatic elements and in those combinations which are relevant to the particular problem. For housing, water conservation, road construction, manufacture, and many other purposes it has periodically been necessary to classify climate according

Note on Figure 1.

Figure 1 is reproduced by permission from *Climatology*, by B. Hauritz and J. M. Austin (New York: McGraw-Hill Book Co., 1944). Only part of the legend is reproduced here. These symbols cover the principal tropical climates. Successive letters indicate degrees of breakdown in the classification.

A. Tropical Rainy Climates
    Af   Tropical rain forest climate
    Am   Tropical monsoon climate
    Aw   Tropical savanna climate

B. Dry Climates
    BW   Desert climate   h denotes a hot B climate
    BS   Steppe climate

C. Warm Temperate Rainy Climates
    Cs   Summer dry
    Cw   Winter dry
    Cfa Without dry season, hot summers
    Cfb Without dry season, warm summers

D. Cool Snow-forest Climates

E. Polar Climate
    ETH Polar climate due to high altitude

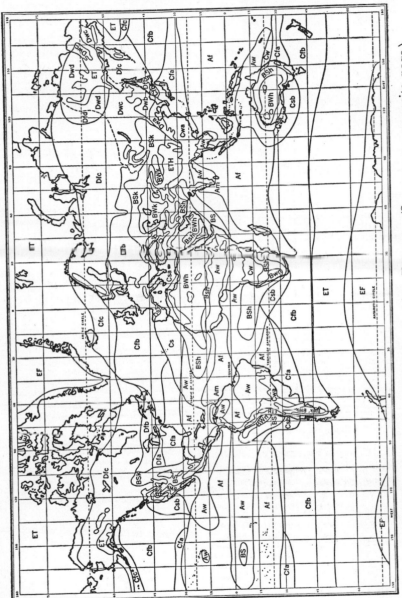

Figure 1. Climatic Types of the Earth, after Köppen. (See note on opposite page.)

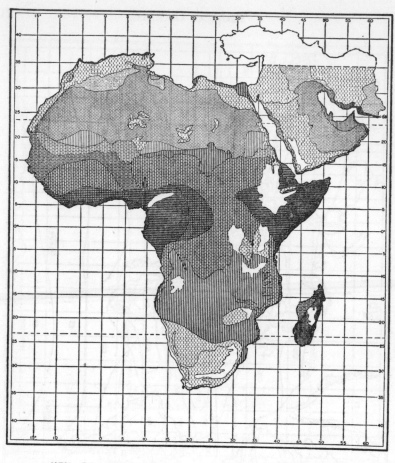

KEY TO SYMBOLS

HATCHING CODE		WARMEST MONTH	COOLEST MONTH
	Hw.Wh	Hot Wet	Warm Humid
	Hw.Wd	Hot Wet	Warm Dry
	Hw.T	Hot Wet	Temperate
	Hh.Wd	Hot Humid	Warm Dry
	Hh.T	Hot Humid	Temperate
	Hd.T	Hot Dry	Temperate
	Hd.C	Hot Dry	Cool
	Ww.Ww	Warm Wet	Warm Wet
	Ww.Wh	Warm Wet	Warm Humid
	Ww.Wd	Warm Wet	Warm Dry
	Ww.T	Warm Wet	Temperate
	Wh.Wh	Warm Humid	Warm Humid
	Wh.Wd	Warm Humid	Warm Dry
	Wh.T	Warm Humid	Temperate
	Wd.Wd	Warm Dry	Warm Dry
	Wd.T	Warm Dry	Temperate
	Wd.C	Warm Dry	Cool

Hot = Mean temp. of month over 86°F.
Warm = Mean temp. of month 68-86°F.
Temperate = Mean temp. of month 50-68°F.
Cool = Mean temp. of month below 50°F.

Wet = Mean vapor pressure of month over 20 mmHg.
Humid = Mean vapor pressure of month 15-20 mmHg.
Dry = Mean vapor pressure of month under 15 mmHg.

Figure 2. Climatic Regions of Africa, Based on Temperature and Vapor Pressure in Hottest and Coolest Months.

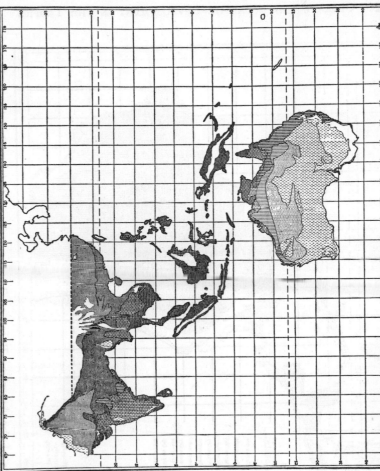

Figure 3. Climatic Regions of the Australo-Asian Region, Based on Temperature and Vapor Pressure in Hottest and Coolest Months.

KEY TO SYMBOLS

HATCHING	CODE	WARMEST MONTH	COOLEST MONTH
	Hw.Wh	Hot Wet	Warm Humid
	Hw.Wd	Hot Wet	Warm Dry
	Hw.T	Hot Wet	Temperate
	Hw.C	Hot Wet	Cool
	Hh.Wd	Hot Humid	Warm Dry
	HhT	Hot Humid	Temperate
	Hd.T	Hot Dry	Temperate
	Hd.C	Hot Dry	Cool
	Ww.Ww	Warm Wet	Warm Wet
	Ww.Wh	Warm Wet	Warm Humid
	Ww.Wd	Warm Wet	Warm Dry
	Ww.T	Warm Wet	Temperate
	Ww.C	Warm Wet	Cool
	Wh.Wh	Warm Humid	Warm Humid
	Wh.Wd	Warm Humid	Warm Dry
	Wh.T	Warm Humid	Temperate
	Wh.C	Warm Humid	Cool
	Wd.T	Warm Dry	Temperate
	Wd.C	Warm Dry	Cool

Hot = Mean temp. of month over 86°F.
Warm = Mean temp. of month 68 - 86°F.
Temperate = Mean temp. of month 50 - 68°F.
Cool = Mean temp. of month below 50°F.

Wet = Mean vapor pressure of month over 20 mmHg.
Humid = Mean vapor pressure of month 15 - 20 mmHg.
Dry = Mean vapor pressure of month under 15 mmHg.

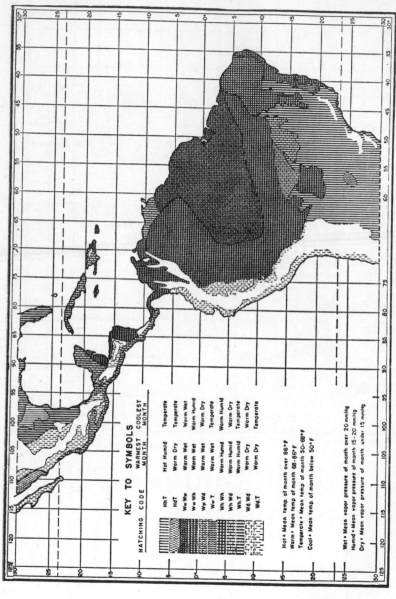

Figure 4. Climatic Regions of the Americas, Based on Temperature and Vapor Pressure in Hottest and Coolest Months.

to the particular circumstances that are involved. None of these classifications, however, is likely to be very useful beyond the type of problem for which it was devised.

CLIMATIC DISTRIBUTION IN THE TROPICS

Although no one set of criteria will serve all purposes, some visual picture is necessary of the way in which climatic patterns do vary from place to place in the tropics if the general principles that will emerge in subsequent chapters are to be considered realistically in relation to specific areas or if, for that matter, the evidence obtained in a given area is to be evaluated in terms of the whole. Figure 1 indicates the distribution of climatic types, according to the Köppen system. The tropical rainy climate (Af and Am according to this classification) covers much of the Indian and Pacific Oceans, but is restricted to smaller bands in the Atlantic Ocean, and extends on to only relatively small portions of the continental masses. By contrast, the tropical savanna climate with dry winters (Aw) occurs more widely over land masses within the solar tropics. The tropical savanna climates tend to be fringed by semi-arid zones, over and to the west of land masses. These, in turn, give way at higher latitudes to the arid climates; but zones of warm temperate rainy climates may intervene. The intruding areas have warm and wet summers, with temperate winters. Scattered among the climatic zones, of course, are numerous areas of fairly high altitude with cooler conditions ranging from warm temperate to polar.

Figures 2, 3, and 4 attempt to express the distribution of climates in relation to their significance for man and animals. Each region is named for the temperature and humidity conditions prevailing in (a) the warmest month and (b) the coolest month. (The warmest month is defined as that following the summer solstice for regions outside the solar tropics, and as that following the second zenith passage of the sun for areas within the tropics. The coolest month is defined as that following the winter solstice.) The temperature and humidity conditions were classified as follows:

Temperature:

mean temperature of month: over 86° F — hot
68°-86° F — warm
50°-68° F — temperate
under 50° F — cool

Humidity (hot and warm months only):

mean vapor pressure of month: over 20 mmhg — wet
15-20 mmhg — humid
under 15 mmhg — dry

The classification is more detailed than that used in the Köppen maps, so that some consolidation may be permitted in description. Climates which vary over the year only from warm wet to warm humid occupy much of equatorial Africa, the entire Amazon basin, and most of Southeast Asia from the southern Indian coasts to New Guinea. Alternating warm humid and warm dry seasons occur in central Africa, in fringe areas to the north and south of equatorial Africa, over the Caribbean and its mainland fringes, and in south central India. Greater seasonal contrasts, between hot wet or warm humid summer conditions and temperate or cold winter conditions, occur in the more southerly regions of Africa, in Argentina and south Brazil, the northern part of the Gulf of Mexico coast, much of India and Indochina, and northeast Australia. Hot dry or warm dry summers alternate with temperate winters in northern Africa, coastal Peru, and a large part of Australia. More or less permanent warm dry conditions persist in coastal Ecuador.

It will be clear from these maps that any attempt to divide the world with bold strokes into a small number of regions with uniform climate would obscure the essential variability. Variegated though they are, the maps show only a small part of the actual variation. Small areas or narrow coastal strips which differ significantly from surrounding areas—such as the high-humidity strip along the western margin of the Persian Gulf—disappear when small maps are made. Yet these limited areas may play an important part in the economy of the region, either by favoring important activities or by imposing special burdens upon commercial undertakings. For practical purposes these and even more restricted "microclimatic" variations may be of considerable importance. Because of advantageous contours, exposure to breezes, drainage, natural vegetation, and other local features, pleasant and nonstressful conditions may well obtain in areas which appear, by and large, to be rather unattractive. In the absence of careful surveys and intelligent planning, on the other hand, commercial and domestic life may be made unnecessarily burdensome and depressing.

Chapter 3

CROP PRODUCTION

"THE LOW LEVEL of food production in the underdeveloped areas of the world, and the wide disparities between food consumption in these areas and in the more advanced countries, have long been recognized as constituting one of the outstanding problems of the world's food and agricultural situation." The Food and Agriculture Organization of the United Nations follows up these words in its contribution to the *Preliminary Report on the World Social Situation* (48b) by numerous tables which show quite clearly that conditions, bad enough before World War II, were made considerably worse by the political and economic disruption which followed. No one table can be taken as conclusive evidence by itself since the reliability of the basic data is sometimes poor. But when several tables all show up tropical countries in a poor light, their combined significance is great.

The figures given in Table 4 indicate a shortage of calories in the diet in even some of the more advanced tropical

Table 4

AVERAGE DIETARY SUPPLY OF CALORIES AS
COMPARED WITH REQUIREMENTS (48b)

Region and country	Recent level[1]	Estimated requirements	Percentage difference
Far East			
Ceylon[2]	1970	2270	−13.2
India	1700	2250	−24.4
Japan	2100	2330	−9.9
Philippines	1960	2230	−12.1
Middle East			
Cyprus	2470	2510	−1.6
Egypt	2290	2390	−4.2
Turkey	2480	2440	+1.6

Table 4 (cont.)

Region and country	Recent level[1]	Estimated requirements	Percentage difference
Africa			
French North Africa	1920	2430	−20.9
Mauritius	*2230*	*2410*	*−7.5*
Union of South Africa	2520	2400	+5.0
Latin America			
Argentina	3190	2600	+22.7
Brazil	*2340*	*2450*	*−4.5*
Chile	2360	2640	−10.6
Mexico	*2050*	*2490*	*−17.6*
Uruguay	2580	2570	+0.4
Europe			
Denmark	3160	2750	+14.9
France	2770	2550	+8.6
Greece	2510	2390	+5.0
Italy	2340	2440	−4.1
Norway	3140	2850	+10.2
United Kingdom	3100	2650	+16.9
North America and Oceania			
Australia	3160	2620	+20.6
United States	3130	2640	+18.5

[1] Precise dates not given in source.
[2] In this and subsequent tables predominantly tropical countries will be in italics.

countries. The situation may well be worse than shown in other countries for which statistics are lacking.

That this relative deficiency in food energy is not only due to inadequate distribution or low purchasing power, but is rooted in poor productivity of the land, is indicated by Table 5.

While local prejudices may account for low productivity per hectare in one particular item, a poor return in six or seven items cannot be explained by any adventitious circumstance.

Data of this kind, showing a widespread lack of productivity in cultivated tropical land, could be cited almost ad

Table 5

PRODUCTIVITY OF LAND PLANTED TO MAJOR CROPS,
1954 (13e, 1955)
(100 kg/hectare)

Region	Wheat	Rye	Barley	Oats	Maize	Rice (paddy)	Potatoes
Europe	15.8	15.2	17.8	16.3	12.5	42.2	147.2
North and Central America	11.1	9.4	13.8	12.4	21.3	24.2	153.8
South America	12.9	7.6	12.6	12.4	12.7	16.1	53.4
Asia	9.0	7.7	10.8	8.8	10.9	16.5	69.7
Africa	8.1	—	6.7	6.6	9.8	13.0	65.6
Oceania	10.8	—	10.1	5.9	19.3	—	100.0

Note: Excludes USSR.

infinitum. Total production is clearly inadequate for the population, and productivity per unit of cultivated land is undoubtedly low. But further questions arise. Is this low productivity due to climatic conditions alone, or to the poverty and ignorance of the peasant or subsistence farmer, or to a combination of the two? It is necessary, therefore, to examine the evidence for the proposition that climate has a deleterious effect upon soil fertility in tropical and subtropical regions.

THE EFFECTS OF CLIMATE

Frequent and heavy precipitation, fairly high temperatures, and the consequent high humidities affect almost every phase of agriculture, sometimes beneficially, but more often disadvantageously. Herein lies what is probably the most significant problem for tropical development. To appreciate it adequately, the various facets must be understood.

On Soils

Most of the nutrients that plants obtain from the soil are soluble. In areas of high rainfall they are easily carried away in the run-off, or are carried down to relatively great depths in the soil by percolation or leaching. In leached soils the nutrients may be picked up by deep-rooted plants, especially by trees, and put back into the soil-plant-soil cycle. But minerals and nitrogenous nutrients which escape this cycle—

whether they are washed away to rivers and the sea, or
deposited as iron pan or bauxite—represent a permanent
depletion, a shrinkage of the nutrient currency. There is a
greater tendency, therefore, for tropical soils to become progressively poorer in essential plant nutrients.

The rock residues remaining after the solution processes will be
either quartz grains (sand) or a heavy clay; the liberated iron
compounds precipitate as "shot" or "laterite," locking up with
them what phosphorus they can obtain from the soil moisture.
These are the reasons for the poor sandy soils of vast areas, or
the unbelievably deep sticky clays, and the absence of any available "road metal" or source of broken rock for road surfacing.
Easily packing but fragile laterite is often the only road surfacing
available. Vast portions of tropical Africa and South America
have been stable tectonically for enormously long periods of
time, and this has retarded the opportunities for geological erosion, which would have facilitated the removal of the leached
out (senile) surface soils, low in plant nutrients. (Pendleton)[1]

The degenerative process may be slowed or stopped by
deep-rooted plants, particularly by trees. The virgin tropical
forest exists simply because it has been able to check the
wastage by taking back from the soil through its deep-root
system the equivalent of the nutrients that it sheds upon the
surface in leaves, branches, and trunks. Assisted by many elements in the complex ecology—fungi, bacteria, termites, animals—the turnover is rapid; but the capital is comparatively
slender and the balance precarious. The lush appearance of
the jungle is as deceptive as the frantic activity of a business
working on a small margin. Under the circumstances which
gave it birth it may well persist indefinitely, but a period of
stress or disturbance may well break the tenuous cycle and
bring disaster. In a very few years man can so dissipate the
tropics' slender capital that recovery is made virtually impossible.

Trees are a useful and effective cover crop when used in rotation with annual food or fiber subsistence or commercial crops.

[1] Quotations with name but no reference are taken from manuscripts
submitted to the Study Group of the Council on Foreign Relations.

Thus for shifting cultivation forest trees, often re-growth stands of well-known trees, are very effective for restoring a modicum of plant nutrients to the surface soil from deep below the surface, as well as for pest elimination, control of Imperata grasses, and physical improvement. But if the soil is really senile and leached out by heavy rains, while there has been no addition of nutrients or removal of the surface soil by geologic erosion, a forest will not often return to the land, nor can it be restored without some source of nutrients (dust, volcanic ash, silt from floods, or commercial fertilizer). (Pendelton)

To certain favored areas nature is free in giving with one hand what she takes away with the other. Rivers which flow quietly through level plains frequently overflow their banks in the flood-period and deposit mineral-bearing silt on land which has been losing its minerals during the rest of the year. This is seen near the Amazon and its major tributaries and on the lower reaches of Southeast Asian rivers; it has been the nourishment of Egypt for seven thousand years. Such generosity, however, can be only at the expense of the mountain and upland regions composing the watershed. Another act of generosity, with drawbacks, however, occurs when mineral-rich volcanic dust settles on land and confers upon it a productivity not shared by nearby lands. This effect can be readily seen, for example, along the western side of Central America.

On Plants

A multiplicity of species and subspecies with relatively few individuals in any one, is characteristic of tropical regions. Only a mixed population with varying demands can exist where the physical situation encourages reproduction and survival but the store of any one requirement is limited. From the very large number of species and varieties of plants that may be found in tropical vegetation, it is only to be expected that there will be many which are useful to man. Indeed, it was this which prompted so much interest by temperate countries in the development of tropical trade. But the possibilities of exploitation are limited by the scattered way in which the plants occur and the difficulty of maintaining pure stands free from disease.

As might be expected, tropical plants tend to be poor in nitrogenous constituents which must be manufactured from the precarious supplies in the soil. On the other hand they are relatively rich in carbohydrate which can be synthesized by the plant from carbon dioxide in the air and the abundant water. Sugar, manioc, rice, corn, and sweet potatoes are familiar examples of tropical foodstuffs rich in carbohydrate but relatively poor in protein.

As might also be expected, it is difficult to grow plants native to temperate zones in tropical regions. The climatic pattern, as well as the shortage of nutrients, is unfavorable. Too much rain, irregular rain, diminished seasonal variation, and changed periodicity of daylight are among the circumstances to which many temperate species cannot become adapted. Mountainous areas within the geographic tropics provide a more amenable climate, but the diminished photoperiodicity is still unsuitable for many temperate plants.

On Diseases and Pests

As was pointed out above, the conflict between two outstanding characteristics of the tropics—the general suitability of the climate for reproduction, growth, and survival, on the one hand, and the shortage of specific nutrients on the other, favors the development of a large variety of living forms with relatively few individuals in any one species. In this complex ecology a pure stand of any one plant variety is automatically at a disadvantage; but potential disease agents are not. Among the multiplicity of living forms, there is a good chance that an agent already exists which will thrive by attacking the plant, or, if it does not exist at the moment, that it will soon appear. Once disease agent and plant have been brought together, the former will flourish at the expense of the latter until both are reduced to the general state of a small number of individuals leading a life of precarious coexistence. Monocultures are particularly susceptible to the onslaught of diseases which were previously rare or unknown.

This holds true even in temperate climates, as is shown by the experience of the soybean industry in the United States. (Over the last twenty years soybean cultivation has expanded nine-fold in acreage and twelve-fold in production, to give an annual crop valued at $750 million. But in the course of this development ten big diseases have emerged from obscurity—four of them quite unknown twelve years ago— and now cause damage estimated at $10 million a year). Under tropical conditions such infestations could easily become widespread epidemics with disastrous results. Blights which have thus affected the cotton, cacao, rubber, and banana industries in the past await the monocultures of the future.

It matters little whether the agent be a microbe, an insect, a larger animal, or a plant form; the principle remains the same: pure stands invite disease. A catalog of the diseases and pests now known would be an extensive one, but it would contain the names only of those which have hitherto had an opportunity to develop. It is impossible to say how rapidly the list would swell if agricultural conditions in the tropics were radically changed or new plants brought under cultivation. However, lest too gloomy a view be taken of the possibility of commercial tropical crops, it must be remembered that there are a few, and important, species that have weathered the hazards of pure stands. Rice is the outstanding example, revealing a surprising adaptation to difficult conditions, as well as an ability to grow well on very poor soils. Manioc is relatively resistant, as is maize. Sugar cane is practically always grown alone and on extensive areas; but here resistance to disease is constantly being reinforced by man through the development of new strains and other preventive measures.

On Management

Tropical climates influence crop management very considerably by reason of the circumstances already considered. The nature of the crop to be grown, the necessity for conserving soil and plant nutrients, and the never-ending war against diseases and pests, all impose upon the grower special duties and practices. Over and above these, other requirements are set by the direct effect of climate upon operations. The effects which most readily come to mind are the difficulty of using wheeled vehicles in the ever-present soft, wet, sticky clay, and the problem of working soil satisfactorily when it is in such a state. Simple manual methods may often be the only ones feasible, and dependence upon mechanization an illusory dream.

A further difficulty resulting directly from the warm and humid conditions is the rapid rate of weed growth. Mechanization may speed the clearance of weeds between rows, but hand work is necessary to clear them away between plants. In the cultivation of rice the flooding and transplanting of the paddies serves to control weeds, which would soon take over the area if cultivation by United States methods were attempted in the true tropics.

Harvesting may have to be closely regulated by the season. A certain stage of development is required in sugar cane, for instance, before the concentration of sugar repays extraction. If the monsoonal rains break before the crop is cut, budding may seriously reduce the concentration once more and force the crop to be held over to the next season. The net result of these various effects of climate upon harvesting is to increase the dependence upon labor and to make more difficult the introduction of labor-saving mechanization.

On Storage and Handling

Food substances, by their very nature, provide an ideal medium for the growth of countless bacteria and molds, and nourishment for all forms of destructive pests. A warm, humid climate greatly increases the chance of infection and accelerates the rate of destruction. These processes can be checked if the storage temperature is reduced to a level not far above freezing by refrigeration, the moisture content removed by dehydration, the more attractive components removed by refining, or growth-preventing chemicals introduced. Such procedures, however, are generally expensive, call for expert control, or detract from the food value of the product. The speed and perfection with which protection must be given in tropical climates increase the difficulty and tend to make the product correspondingly more expensive. In addition to the processing plant required for these purposes, storage facilities for both the raw and the processed product must be erected with considerable care, so that they provide protection from rain and vermin without trapping heat or encouraging condensation when the temperature falls. In the absence of adequate storage facilities, large seasonal and even annual fluctuations in prices may be caused.

CIRCUMVENTING THE EFFECTS

Such are the many obstacles tropical climates impose on crop production. It has been necessary to list the adverse effects of tropical climate upon agriculture in some detail so that the enemy may be recognized and wishful thinking discouraged. But, to the gloomy picture thus drawn there is, fortunately, a brighter side. We do know something about circumventing climatic effects; we are in a position to do better than we have in the past; and our knowledge is increasing. On some sectors we may even be able to move from the defense to the attack. If the net effect of climate upon crop production is to be correctly assessed, these defensive or counteroffensive measures must be taken into account.

On Soils

The preservation of trees is one very desirable method of conservation. The primitive subsistence practice of burning off the natural forest, growing crops for a few years until the soil is exhausted, and then abandoning the area to repeat the process all over again elsewhere, can be exceedingly destructive, as is testified by the extensive tropical areas now supporting coarse and useless Imperata grasses. But a controlled form of this "shifting cultivation" has been practiced for centuries without marked deterioration where the subsistence culture has recognized the problem and encouraged regrowth of trees by restricting the areas burned, limiting the number of shallow crops grown, and replanting the area with useful trees when it is abandoned. It must be realized, however, that one can hardly speak of economic development where subsistence farming of this nature is perpetuated.

Moreover, a large area is required for the maintenance of a few people by such practices.

A type of strip-farming, in which limited areas are cleared and planted to low crops while the surrounding forest is left intact, is one form of compromise; although it remains to be seen how long a forest remains intact once cleared areas are established within it.

Here is the strength of the Belgian Congo's "corridor system," a rationalization of kaingining ("shifting cultivation"). In this method the forest is cleared a little at a time, say one acre per planting season, by each family. Food crops, such as upland rice and maize, are planted first; then cotton as a money crop; and finally cassava and bananas are planted together as a food crop. The cassava is dug after two years, while the banana plants continue to bear and shade the soil sufficiently to maintain an appropriate micro-climate for the germination and development of native forest trees. These will ultimately choke out the bananas as they develop into a new forest. After growing for ten, fifteen, or more years (the length of time is not known) the productive capacity of the soil will have been restored, and the forest can be cleared and again cropped. (Pendleton)

Contours must be carefully chosen and the length of strips limited if erosion and leaching or the washing out of soluble nutrients are to be minimized.

The gradual substitution of commercial trees for non-productive trees is another method of conservation, but this is likely to introduce the dangers of pure stands unless the proportion of substitution is restricted. In commercial stands, such as those of rubber trees, it is important to let most of the underbrush remain, since it plays an important stabilizing role in the complex ecology and helps to control erosion.

Mixed cultivation of low and high crops sometimes provides a profitable compromise. Bananas, for example, can provide essential shade for cacao plants. The practice in India of planting mixed grains allows the slender soil resources to be shared among plants with somewhat different demands, but poses something of a problem for harvesting and constitutes one of the difficulties in the way of mechanization.

The destructive effects of floods can be controlled, and the benefit of the water and dissolved minerals spread over a wider area by irrigation systems. In many areas the measures for irrigating the soil must be combined with provisions for draining it when there is an excess of water.

The replacement of lost minerals and nitrogenous compounds by the addition of fertilizers is a solution which comes readily to the mind of present-day Western man; but such a program is fraught with difficulties in many tropical regions. In the first place, factory-produced fertilizers are expensive and are often beyond the means of the country concerned, even without the added cost of transportation. Second, the use of fertilizers presupposes a knowledge of what substances are deficient in the soil, the relative acidity of the soil, and the specific requirements of the particular crop. Whereas these facts may be fairly well known for temperate situations, they are very poorly known for tropical areas. Finally, it hardly appears sensible to pour in fertilizer each year, only to have it go out to sea with the next rain. Some control must be introduced over the annual loss by leaching before artificial replenishment can be viewed with equanimity.

The time may come when fertilizers will be economically justified, but in many areas that time is not yet. There is perhaps more point to the utilization of green manure, especially where the manuring crop fixes atmospheric nitrogen; yet it cannot be blithely assumed that legumes will automatically do this. Both the species and the conditions must be right before the nitrogen-fixing bacteria can operate. Animal wastes may be used, although in many areas the diet of the animal is so poor that the excreta have very little value as manure. In some areas, such as India, it is considered more important to dry the dung for fuel than to apply it to the fields.

On Species

With the exception of rice and, perhaps, the sweet potato, the genetic potentialities of tropical plants have not been well explored. (The developments achieved in maize have been related mainly to nontropical environments.) Among the numerous varieties of a useful plant some are certain to be more useful, more resistant, or more adaptable than others. Experimental breeding may result in better types, as it has so often with temperate crops, and perpetual hybridization may conceivably make possible a vast improvement in tropical plants such as has been achieved with corn. It would seem that here is an important possibility for future development, which might be still further extended if the potentialities of temperate plants for adaptation to tropical conditions were systematically examined.

In attempting to breed new types with specific qualities, care must be taken that the element of "ruggedness," which wild forms commonly have, is not lost. In some respects, a general ability to withstand stress is as important as a well-developed specific characteristic, especially where the climate is erratic and periods of high humidity and warmth may be followed by drought or cold. But this hazard is fairly well known and detracts little from the general proposition that genetic studies should greatly improve future possibilities.

On Disease

The agriculturalist faced with the problem of disease must adopt a somewhat different approach from that used by the medical scientist. On the one hand he has a tremendous advantage in that he can hope to breed a stock that is relatively immune to the disease. On the other, his opportunity for treating developed disease is usually very limited. Aside from breeding, therefore, he must place his main reliance on preventive measures by making conditions unsuitable for the development of the disease or by removing sources of infection. Methods which are successful in temperate climates may be ineffective under tropical circumstances, either because the disease agent is different, or because the climatic conditions interfere with the measures. These, however, are technical difficulties which can almost certainly be overcome if sufficient attention is given to the new problem or to the new setting of an old problem. The techniques and research methods which have provided essential information about rusts, parasitic worms, or insect vectors[2] of viral disease should

[2] A vector is a living agent which carries disease-producing agents without itself necessarily showing disease.

be equally effective in elucidating tropical plant diseases. There will always be a remnant of ill-understood disease, but there seems little reason to believe that this residue should be any greater in the tropics than elsewhere. What may make progress more difficult in tropical areas is the multiplicity of disease forms, and the good chance that as one is vanquished a new one may appear. Nevertheless, the future appears much brighter than the past.

On Methods

Much trouble has arisen in the past through failure to realize that different conditions in the tropics may call for different methods of harvesting, processing, and storage than those which had proved successful in temperate countries. The climatic conditions certainly compel such changes. Soft, wet clay, of which there is so much in the tropics, may require larger bearing surfaces and greater power in vehicles, or lighter construction. Rust-resistant coatings and avoidance of electrolytic metal contacts are more necessary.

The mode of plowing must be adapted to the circumstances of the place and season to prevent erosion either by heavy rain or by wind, and yet permit permeation of the soil by light rains. Upon occasion it may be desirable to turn up subsoil which contains some of the deeply permeating minerals; at other times such a practice would only increase erosion and leaching. By a judicious selection from conservation techniques which are already well known—contour plowing, corrugated farming, terracing, stripcropping, rotation, and interplanting—and by adaptation of the principles to detailed local conditions, a great deal can be done to restrict deterioration and improve fertility.

But in many instances it will be advisable to retain some of the manual methods of the indigenous peoples and to integrate these with the mechanical procedures employed in temperate countries. The simple lake culture of the Aztecs was apparently well suited to their social organization: "native" rubber contributed importantly to the economy of Malaya; the simplest of manual methods enable the Indian peasant to get for his own use almost the maximum that his land will yield in default of fertilizer.

As to storage, some of the worst effects of the climate can be controlled by attention to the design of storehouses. By and large, totally enclosed buildings are not suitable. Rain must certainly be excluded, but free perflation by natural breezes must be encouraged and supplemented, if necessary, by forced ventilation. Containers should similarly be freely permeated by air if condensation is to be avoided. Inside temperatures will be reduced if the roof is adequately insulated and ventilation arranged in such a way that heated air passes directly to the exterior. Vermin may be discouraged by screening openings well and by separating the stored material in relatively small parcels. As refrigeration becomes technically more reliable and cheaper, its use may be considerably extended. Primitive drying methods may be supplemented in many instances by relatively inexpensive and easily operated equipment, such as fans, air heaters, or infrared bulbs. Regional canning is already saving many crops and stabilizing markets where confusion and loss were formerly frequent occurrences.

COMPLICATING FACTORS

It is clear that the adverse effects of tropical climates may be countered in many ways, but a number of nonclimatic circumstances may complicate the picture by influencing either the opportunity for climate to affect soils and crops or the measures taken to control and combat those effects. Before the net effect of climate can be seen in true perspective, therefore, it is necessary to review the more important complicating factors.

Systems of Land Tenure

To the extent that a particular system of land tenure encourages the agricultural worker to improve the yield, to conserve the soil nutrients, and to increase his own efficiency, it is a good system insofar as the primary purpose of production is concerned. To the extent that it fails to do these things, or actually discourages them, it is a bad system. Considerations of the ethical aspects of a system, important though they may be, are not relevant to the present discussion.

The type of land tenure may affect production through

the ability to provide material requirements, such as implements, seed, and marketing facilities; or psychological requirements such as encouragement, guidance, and recompense. This holds true for all agriculture, temperate as well as tropical—indeed for all industry. The particular relevance to the present discussion is that while the agricultural problems of the tropics call for particular care and understanding, the systems of land ownership prevailing in those regions frequently frustrate their solution. The following extract from the United Nations *Preliminary Report on the World Social Situation* (48b) indicates how real this problem has been in some parts of Latin America, for example, and how much the land may be neglected just where it most needs special care.

This uneven distribution of population in Latin America—and the failure to make the most effective use of its total immense area—is closely related to the systems of land use, of settlement and of land tenure which prevail. Control of the land has traditionally been associated with political and economic power and social prestige. Large-scale agricultural enterprise, with the control of work opportunities vested in the hands of a few landowning families or corporations, is still [1952] characteristic of great areas. The land-holding classes of Latin America, schooled in the traditions of land as a symbol of prestige, are given to speculative production on the one hand, and to the practice of maintaining large tracts of idle but inaccessible land on the other. Land resources of the region have been diminishing for centuries, because of inefficient methods of cultivation, such as fire agriculture [brush-burning], lack of fertilizer, deforestation, erosion, etc. At the same time, the concentration in ownership, often without full use of the land, has aggravated the problem of land pressure.

At the other end of the scale, and sometimes paradoxically associated with the type of neglect just described, is the practice of minute subdivision into holdings which are far below the optimum size for efficient management. In such instances, the individual farmer cannot obtain credit for improvement or arrange crops so that the failure of one may be offset by success with another. In some countries inheritance customs not only tend to divide land into ever smaller portions, but also scatter the lots owned by one individual over a wide territory, so that no efficient management can be contemplated by the owner.

At the time it was written (1952), the extract given above probably represented a widespread state of affairs, but circumstances were already changing, and considerable improvements have been effected since in many areas. The desirable modifications are by no means yet complete; indeed, one could not expect drastic reform to be accomplished rapidly without precipitating a dangerous state of social instability. The following comments on land tenure in other tropical regions, abstracted from the same United Nations report, similarly describe social conditions that are becoming less and less characteristic, but where they still persist, they complicate the picture of climatic effects.

In certain parts of the Middle East a large part of the tenant's production may revert to the landowner, who may or may not contribute anything worthwhile in the way of enlightened guidance, management, or economic cushioning. Under the less desirable landlords the cultivator lacks the motivation for harder or more thoughtful effort and is unable to obtain the necessary assistance when he does try to develop. In some areas of Southeast Asia, "where the holding is small or the rent particularly high, the advance of grain to feed the tenant's family until the harvest is reaped is part of the agreement—a part without which the tenant often cannot exist, as his own share in the produce is not large enough to see him through the year. The [less scrupulous] landlord, by means of this advance, obtains a hold over the tenant that permits him to exact additional services, as occasion may arise—services not specified in the [usually] verbal agreement. . . . Such services . . . can be extremely onerous. The demand for them rises with increased tenant competition for the land." (48b)

Within any one system, of course, there is wide variation with the knowledge and social attitude of the owner or manager. Some very large estates are administered in such a way that the individual farmer is given every encouragement to be an efficient producer; and some quite idealistic schemes are ruined by a lack of understanding on the part of those exercising influence. Nor can the role of government be ignored—in fact, a good case be made for the proposition that the role of government for good or bad is even more influential in the less-developed countries than it is in those which are more technologically developed.

Lack of Communications

Trade outlets are obviously essential to any agriculture above the mere subsistence level. But rapid and widespread communications are essentially an achievement of the last hundred years, introduced only sporadically into tropical settings, and then often primarily in the interests of temperate commerce. However suitable other factors may be for encouraging agricultural development, rapid progress cannot be expected until adequate means are provided for the delivery of products to the purchaser and the return transport of exchange goods to the landed consumer.

As well as any, this requirement illustrates the complex interactive nature of the problem lying behind the apparently simple question, "What is the role of climate in the economic development of the tropics?" Climate affects crop production, and some of these effects can be overcome; but the increased yield calls for rapid transportation. Transportation, however, is hard to come by unless there is first a reasonable guarantee of increased crops; and transportation itself is affected by climate. No one factor stands alone; each depends upon others. In dealing with such a complex situation we must first examine each facet alone; but the limitations of the analytic approach must be recognized, and a synopsis attempted before operating decisions are made. Some further consideration will be given to this problem in Chapter 7.

Conservatism, Ignorance, Poverty

This self-perpetuating triad probably impresses the visitor to the tropics more than any other characteristic, partly because it is so widespread, but partly also because it so strongly resists argument. The problem is by no means new, nor is it uniquely tropical. One would find much the same state of affairs if transported back to medieval Europe, or even today in some isolated areas of the United States. It is relevant to the present discussion, not because it is unique to the tropics, but because it is so widespread there and interferes so markedly with attempts to counter adverse climatic effects.

Unless a real desire for improvement is awakened in the minds of individual farmers, neither equipment nor advice can hope to win a substantial improvement in production. Education is certainly needed, but formal education is not enough. A very personal type of education is required, in which the interest of the individual farmer is engaged, but antagonism avoided. Slow and demanding as it is, this kind of education is absolutely essential in the early stages at least. The scheme for the formation of village development agencies formulated by the government of India (19) exemplifies the procedures required.

Once awakened, the desire for improvement will automatically create some of the means for achieving it; but further measures will still be necessary if the high hopes thus raised are not to be dashed. Material assistance in putting the new ideas to work and measures to ensure some encouraging reward to the individual for his work will be necessary at the outset if the newly awakened faith is to survive. Occasionally the process will start to move so suddenly and gain momentum so quickly that the well-wisher will find it necessary to apply some brake; but this embarrassing position of dissuading where he was so recently urging, is an almost gratifying form of frustration.

REQUIRED ACTION

We have seen that agricultural production tends to be at very low levels in the tropics and that tropical climates impose many difficulties which may account for a significant part of that deficiency. But we have also seen that the adverse climatic effects can in large measure be countered and that many of the ills that beset tropical agriculture are social or economic rather than climatic. Practical interest demands that some indication be given of ways in which the results of the foregoing analysis can be utilized—ways in which production can be increased in spite of the obvious difficulties that it faces.

Very seldom in human affairs can action be limited to just one aspect if it is to be successful. Nevertheless, in reviewing the evidence and in formulating policy, a certain subdivision is necessary to avoid confusion. To this end the problem of agricultural development in the tropics may be considered under the three headings of management, research, and education. It must be remembered, however, that the three lines of action need to be closely related and that it is not sufficient merely to trust this to the natural course of events or even to a "coordinating authority" set up for the purpose. There must be a spirit of cooperation, a ruling concept of combined attack for a common goal, if real results are to be achieved.

We of the technological world are so conscious of the importance of such attributes as "man management," "public relations," "get-up-and-go," that we are apt to err in our assessment of the tropical situation. Paradoxically, we simultaneously underestimate and overestimate the potentialities of local leadership—underestimate the proportion of persons capable of adapting to technology, overestimate the extent to which they will be impressed by the advantages of a technological culture. The stimulus must come from our end; but it must be applied in continuing fashion over fairly long periods of time, and it must expect the results to be qualitatively different from those which characterize our cultures. The short, sharp presentation on a take-it-or-leave-it basis which characterizes much of the salesmanship here will produce more opponents than disciples when applied in a culture where time is traditionally a divine gift and not a disposable commodity.

Management

Undoubtedly we already know a certain amount about the difficulties created for agriculture by tropical climates and the methods of circumventing them. Undoubtedly, also, we are not making the best use of this knowledge. Considerable improvement could be wrought simply by putting existing knowledge to work. A review of the numerous recommendations made in 1949 by a large number of experts from various countries (48d) should convince any skeptic of the immense scope for immediate action. From what has been said in the present short account, an application of the following principles should result in increased or more reliable agricultural production:

Restriction of the areas cleared and burned for "shifting cultivation," with abolition of the practice at the earliest possible date.

Retention of tree cover in conjunction with low crops.

Gradual substitution of selected for natural trees, with limitation of the proportion of any one species.

Preservation of low covering plants in commercial forests.

Avoidance of monocultures unless experience has shown adequate adaptation.

Conservation of soil by whatever physical methods are applicable to the individual situation.

Utilization of sequestered land.

Development of irrigation to supply water in dry seasons, to add water-borne nutrients, and to control floods.

Reclamation of "salted" areas by washing out through combined flooding and drainage.

Selection of native practices well adapted to physical and cultural conditions.

Introduction of technological methods to the extent that they are adaptable to physical and cultural conditions.

Improvement of storage facilities in both capacity and protective efficiency.

Increase of incentive to the individual agricultural worker.

Judicious use of fertilizers and weed preventives.

Action is imperative; it would be foolish to postpone all endeavor until all the facts are available. Action must be taken in the light of the best knowledge available; but this action should be taken with conscious realization of the shortcomings of the skills and intelligence at hand and, if at all possible, it should be action along lines which can be modified as better skills develop. This requirement, as well as the great variety of influencing factors—soils, climates, resources, productivity, human needs, and human attitudes—demands that all policies and plans be flexible.

Such flexibility is as necessary from place to place as it is from time to time. No two problems are identical; no one solution is entirely adequate under two different circumstances. Diametrically opposed, as well as merely different, measures may have to be considered or even combined. Drainage needs to be balanced against irrigation, fertilizers against conservation, selective breeding of local plants against introduction of new types, technology against primitive methods, subsistence against cash crops. Nor are vision and wisdom the least important virtues required of advisers. Until such time as an experienced body of local agriculturalists develops, the initiative in management will undoubtedly lie with the government of the country concerned.

Research

At each turn of the discussion we are brought up against the fact that our knowledge of the variables we are trying to handle is limited. While this is true of knowledge in any field, the inadequacies appear more glaring here than on comparable questions within the temperate zones. It is fairly evident, moreover, that new facts and new knowledge are more difficult to acquire in the tropics, that tropical research is not only more necessary but also more difficult to organize. Herein lies a challenge that cannot be ignored without danger to our welfare as well as our pride. It is a challenge that calls for the closest collaboration between the tropical countries and those with a greater concentration of scientific and technological facilities.

The chemical and physical nature of tropical soils needs to be established over far greater areas than has been possible with the limited surveys hitherto carried out, especially in view of the great diversity in types that these surveys have revealed. Inadequacies will undoubtedly be discovered in current methods of classification, and many new problems brought to light. Problems raised by anomalies of classification, by unexpected or unexplained effects upon fertility, by physical reaction to cultivation practices, by water permeability and capacity, and a host of other practical demands, will require intensive study. Such studies will inevitably demand new physical and chemical techniques and new concepts, just as in every other field of scientific inquiry. As fast as the key to one practical problem emerges, other problems will arise. Some of these will be of direct practical significance, some will concern research techniques, others will be of a fundamental nature; but all will call for attention if knowledge and understanding are to advance and ultimate development be served.

With the intensive study of soils must go detailed inquiries into the soil-plant relationship. Only through a full knowledge of the things required from the soil by plants, the soil conditions necessary to plant welfare, the effects of plants upon the soil, and the substances added to the soil by plants, can optimum use of the soil be contemplated. Such questions as the best depth for plowing; the mechanical state in which the soil should be maintained; the nature, amount, and time of applying fertilizer best suited to plant development; the frequency with which crops should be planted; and numerous similar problems call for precise information of the interrelationships.

It is only reasonable to suppose that what has been done by genetics and plant breeding in the way of increasing resistance to disease, adjusting the growth cycle to the season, and improving the yield might also be done for tropical crops. Some of this has, in fact, been done for rice and for corn; but there are numerous other plants which might be similarly improved, to say nothing of the multitudinous species whose productive possibilities have scarcely been examined. Dramatic results, however, do not spring from a few lucky trials. Behind the well-advertised success there is a long story of systematic inquiry, examination of innumerable possibilities, establishment of basic principles by experiments which may seem to have little or no connection with plant production. The exciting final stages of development follow extensive and often frustrating research without which clues would not have been understood or even seen. Two broad objectives might be cited for research in plant genetics: selection and improvement of tropical species, and adaptation of species introduced from temperate regions. Both are fraught with grave difficulties. Neither can be said at this stage to be more important or promising than the other.

A cardinal principle of disease control is to attack the cycle of disease, and the circumstances which promote that cycle, at all possible points. In this way relative success at one point may be reinforced by relative success at another; or failure at one point counteracted by success at another. Direct attack upon disease agents should not be stopped when resistant varieties are evolved, and certainly should not be neglected simply in the hope that resistance will be developed. There is every indication that the attack on organisms and vectors of disease must not only be continued but increased, and that this requirement will hold for a long time to come. As circumstances change, new plants are brought into production, new diseases emerge, current methods become inadequate, or prevailing ideas prove unsound. Continuing research is as vital to this as to any other scientifically directed endeavor. Developments in the field of human medicine may have considerable significance for the control of plant disease, so that close contact must be maintained between the two groups of investigators. Plant disease, as well as human disease, may be transmitted by insects. Thus, improved methods of insect control may be as important for the one as the other, but initiative in studying methods of control should be conserved for workers in both fields. For the large proportion of plant disease special methods of control must be sought and, in particular, methods which are applicable over wide areas at low cost. This is a program to which there is no visible end.

The idea that "research" is necessary and a good thing is well accepted today in technological countries, but there is still an insufficient appreciation of what is involved. It is not enough to put up a laboratory, to furnish equipment, and to offer good salaries. Somehow or other an interest must be created in the class of problem that will arise, and facilities or opportunities superior to those available in similar fields elsewhere must be provided. It is here that the greatest difficulties are encountered. In most technological countries there are more opportunities for research than can be taken by the available research workers, so that few will experience a desire to look outside of their own environment for satisfaction. Of those who do show an interest, some may be pioneers of the best type, but others may well be those who are chary of facing the keener competition at home. With time, research workers will develop in the tropical countries too, but for many years there will be great difficulty in obtaining high-caliber research workers in the numbers that are required for the task.

Education

Knowledge is not enough; it must be appreciated by those who should apply it. For problems involving crop production and the soil, this means education of the individual farmer—a problem by no means unknown in temperate countries. But there are as many dangers in attempting to apply the educational standards and concepts of technological countries to tropical regions as there are in trying to introduce the technological practices themselves. The concepts and standards must be modified, sometimes radically modified, to fit the different circumstances.

One of the first problems is to awaken a desire for improvement, a willingness to change. The natural conservatism of the poor and ill-informed is accentuated in the tropics by the benignity of the climate. There is little chance of freezing to death; almost anything in the way of clothing and shelter will conserve life; there is no hard winter season to force provision for the months ahead. Existence is comparatively easy, except in grossly overpopulated areas; but anything more may be very difficult—so difficult as to be accepted as virtually unattainable. A realization that existence is not enough and that substantial improvement is both desirable and possible is the first and essential task of education. In the end this means education of the individual agricultural worker; but it may well depend upon an education of persons at more influential levels. It is at this higher level that the technological countries can be more helpful, since the conservative poor are more likely to respond to compatriots than to outsiders.

In tropical countries both the subject matter and the mode of presentation must be adapted to the local situation. The presentation needs to be demonstrative and cooperative, not academic or authoritative; the subject matter must be immediately practical, rather than theoretical or visionary. At the same time, the current educational program must be part of a long-range plan for progressive development. Temperate countries participating in such educational programs have to guard against too rapid an imposition of highly technological practices. They also have to exercise more care than is commonly taken in deciding the form of technical and scientific training for local key personnel.

Some of the younger tropical inhabitants may have sufficient scientific training and breadth of vision to benefit from the regular academic programs of temperate countries, and thus provide a reserve of deep understanding for future developments in their own countries. The majority, however, are better served by instruction at a more practical level, specially designed to meet the problems of their particular areas. Such instruction is usually best carried out in their own countries, preferably in their own language, and if necessary, with the assistance of suitable personnel borrowed from technological countries. Local programs of this sort have many advantages: statements can be immediately checked against local facts; the educator himself is educated; the trainees are spared the disturbing influences of living in other cultures; the educational stimulus is felt beyond the immediate ranks of the trainees; and the country develops a conscious pride in its own development. Extension programs have been operating for many years in some tropical countries and provide a ready channel for newer and better ideas to be planted at the grass roots.

The best-intentioned plans will be frustrated, however, if agricultural labor continues to be held in the extremely low esteem that is customary in some tropical countries today. The sharp distinction between educated thinker and ignorant artisan which foiled the development of science under the Ptolemies, will strangle agricultural development in these countries today if it is allowed to persist. The educational program must create the idea of the dignity of labor, without which today's achievements would have been impossible in technological countries. This may take time, tact, and patience; but without it little advance will be made.

As individual productivity increases and as mechanical

methods gradually supersede the manual, a smaller number of agricultural workers will be needed to produce the country's food supply. Some adjustment in the economic structure must, therefore, be anticipated to absorb the excess labor force. This will become necessary sooner—in fact, it is already a problem—in countries with a very high proportion of unskilled labor.

PREFERENTIAL REGIONS

The scope for improvement is vast; but the resources are limited. At any one time there is only a certain amount of effort that can be expended, and only a certain amount of money that can be made available, for assistance to less developed countries. The very pressing question therefore arises as to where this limited assistance could be expected to give the best results. This is somewhat like seeking a system to win at roulette, since so many factors are involved, and their relative importance is so imperfectly understood. In some cases, it must be admitted, political expediency will be the most powerful factor in determining where assistance should be given. But apart from such overriding influences, the conditions that favor success can be fairly simply stated.

Some of the governing factors are climatic, but many are not. A region in which natural events assist development, albeit in an irregular or unreliable fashion, has obvious advantages. Where rivers bring mineral-rich silt which can be spread over leached land, or where volcanoes scatter fertilizing ash, there is certainly hope that the ravages of nature can be controlled, and the benefits conserved by thoughtful engineering. The challenge is stimulating, and the rewards are good. Both improve the chances of success and make the odds more attractive. Where bad seasons are succeeded in fairly regular fashion by good seasons, there is hope that production during the good can be sufficiently increased to tide over the bad, or that the rainfall can be conserved by storage and utilized during drought through irrigation. But when the good seasons are fitful and unreliable, then the chances of success are considerably reduced, and the cost of effort which will be effective at the worst times is greatly increased.

Complete dependence upon mineral resources may be an

economic hazard, but an intelligent utilization of those resources may provide capital for investment in agricultural improvement, which will then give a long-lasting productivity—a process to be witnessed in present-day Venezuela. Many tropical and subtropical countries such as Saudi Arabia and Iraq are in the happy position today of realizing on their valuable mineral resources; but the extent to which the income is being put to wise development varies considerably from one to another.

A most important factor for development is the political stability of the country concerned. It is very difficult to see how what is essentially a long-term program can be successful if those responsible for its sponsorship or conduct are themselves uncertain of tenure or are replaced by others committed to taking a different line of action, or just "changing things." The difficulty is lessened where the essential action is in the hands of a nonpolitical, permanent, or independent body, or where the contending political parties have sanctioned the development. This state of affairs, however, seems to be exceptional in the politically troubled areas of the tropics. It is most unfortunate that political instability today seriously clouds the chances of development in several of these countries.

Finally, the attitude of the people themselves, or of the social organizations which control that attitude, may be quite critical. There are some peoples who do not want "progress" and prefer to remain in their more primitive state. In certain countries powerful organizations fight to prevent change, presumably because of a vested interest in the old way. In either case private investors would hesitate before committing much capital in radically new programs, and friendly governments would be disinclined to offer a large proportion of their limited funds for developmental assistance. The physical climate certainly exercises an important influence upon agricultural development, but only too often it is overshadowed by the political climate and cultural conditions.

Chapter 4

ANIMAL PRODUCTION

THE LINE of argument is sometimes advanced that it is more economic in underdeveloped countries to grow food crops that can be directly consumed by man than to grow feed for animals which will be at best only partially consumed by him. In a general way it may be said that if one acre of land sown to rice will support a family it will require seven acres to support it on meat, milk, and other animal products. No animal converts more than a fraction of the food it consumes into edible flesh or milk.[1] Actually, several factors intrude to compel, or at least to make advisable, the maintenance of a certain proportion of livestock. In at least a few areas there are already large numbers of domestic animals. "India and Pakistan combined have only about 53 per cent of the land area of the United States, yet have about 290 cattle and water buffaloes for every 100 cattle in the United States." (35) Domestic animals enter into the economy of under-developed areas in many ways other than as suppliers of food. Hair and wool are widely used in the manufacture of clothing, tents, and several household articles. Large numbers of draft animals are employed on the farm and in transportation, and will continue to furnish an important fraction of the rural power for some time to come.

Even as a source of human food, animals are not completely replaceable by crops. Side by side with the low calorie intake discussed in the previous chapter, another more subtle, but important, dietary deficiency may be found over large parts of the tropics—shortage of protein, especially animal protein. The improvement of crop production, along the lines indicated in Chapter 3, might make good the caloric deficiency and provide some improvement in protein intake; but the need for much greater amounts of animal

[1] Williams, R. R., "Chemistry as a Supplement to Agriculture in Meeting World Food Needs." *American Scientist.* v. 44, no. 3 (1956), pp. 317-327.

protein would remain. A good though not perfect geographical correlation is found between incidence of kwashiokor (see p. 107) and low consumption of animal proteins. The animal proteins are characterized by a higher content of certain of the eight amino acids essential for proper human nutrition. In general vegetable proteins tend to be lower than animal proteins in lysine, tryptophan, methionine, and perhaps threonine. The cause of kwashioker is presumably to be found in this area.[2] A daily intake of 70 grams of protein, about one half as animal protein, has been recommended as desirable (13b). This recommendation may be compared with the average daily consumption of animal protein in different countries set out in Table 6. In no really

Table 6

AVERAGE INTAKE OF ANIMAL PROTEIN IN
VARIOUS COUNTRIES IN 1950 (13b)

Average intake (grams per day)	Country or territory
over 70	Iceland
60 to 70	Argentina, New Zealand, Australia, Uruguay
50 to 60	Sweden, United States, Denmark, Canada, Norway
40 to 50	Switzerland, Ireland, United Kingdom, Finland
30 to 40	Netherlands, France, Belgium, Czechoslovakia
20 to 30	*Burma*, Union of South Africa, W. Germany, *Colombia*, *Cuba*, *Brazil*, Austria, *Madagascar*, Chile, *El Salvador*, *Honduras*, Morocco, Poland, *Ethiopia*, Spain
10 to 20	Italy, *Philippines*, Portugal, *Mexico*, Hungary, Greece, E. Germany, *Thailand*, Turkey, Cyprus, Pakistan, *Tanganyika*, *Mauritius*, Yugoslavia, Egypt, *Ceylon*
0 to 10	Algeria, *Peru*, Tunisia, *Indo-China*, Japan, *India*, Syria and Lebanon, China, *Indonesia*

tropical country is the recommended level (35 grams per day) exceeded; in many the intake is less than half the stipulated amount; and in some it is almost negligible.

[2] Williams, R. R., cited, quoting Brock, J. F., et al., "Kwashiokor and Protein Nutrition," *Lancet,* Aug. 20, 1955.

The factors responsible for the low consumption of animal protein are numerous and vary from place to place, but one important cause lies in the poor productivity of the individual animals. The better meat animals in the tropics compare favorably in size with the average of those slaughtered in the southeast of the United States, but unfavorably with the average for the whole of the United States (Table 7). The vast majority of the meat animals in the tropics, however, are much less productive than this (35).

Table 7

COMPARISON OF BEEF YIELDS IN UGANDA AND THE UNITED STATES

Region		Average live weight at slaughter (lbs.)	Average carcass weight as % of live weight
North central U.S.A.[a]	1952	1008	—
Southeast U.S.A.[b]	1952	735	—
All U.S.A.	1944-53	924-992	55
Uganda (Serere)	Cows, heifers	598	48
Uganda (Serere)	Oxen	730	48.5

Notes: a Illinois, Iowa, Michigan, Minnesota, Wisconsin.
     b Alabama, Florida, Georgia, Louisiana, Mississippi.
Sources: For the United States, (49a, 1953); for Uganda, (15a).

Again, the low productivity of the individual animal is well seen in data on milk yield given in Table 8.

The low level of milk production is the more serious since the efficiency of conversion of animal feed to human food is greater in the case of the milk cow than for any other animal, except the pig. Furthermore, milk consumption is less subject to cultural taboos than most meats.

The low productivity of domestic animals in the tropics is not confined to meat and milk, but frequently extends to such qualities as wool and hair growth. Table 9 indicates the wide range in productivity of the individual animal, from one country to another; but it must be remembered that the importance of wool to the economy, and thus the

Table 8

AVERAGE ANNUAL MILK PRODUCTION

(lbs. per milking cow)

Region	Production[1]	Region	Production
North Central		Indonesia	4,140
United States[2]	9,165	Malaya (Fed. States)	835
Southeast		Pakistan	705
United States[3]	6,430		
Netherlands	8,360	Bechaunaland	3,720
Australia	4,040	Egypt	1,035
		Egypt: Damietta	2,330
Jamaica	3,880	Holstein	5,589
Nicaragua	2,445	Eritrea	3,170
Puerto Rico	2,925	French Somaliland	1,365
Ecuador	2,485	Northern Rhodesia	1,035
Brazil	1,430	Nyasaland	265
Surinam	2,045	Somalia	1,800
Venezuela	1,585	Southern Rhodesia	1,890
		Southwest Africa	1,450
Ceylon		Uganda: Nganda	2,087
European	3,750	Zebu	1,940
Indian	2,500	Zanzibar	1,722
India	420		
India (approved farms)	4,100		

[1] Averages for different years.
[2] Illinois, Iowa, Michigan, Minnesota, Wisconsin.
[3] Alabama, Florida, Georgia, Louisiana, Mississippi.
Sources: For the United States, (9); for India (approved farms), (22a & b); for Ceylon, (57); for Egypt, (43); for Uganda and Zanzibar, (15a); for all others, (13a).

attention given to developing highly productive types, also varies. Although it is difficult to obtain satisfactory data, there is reason to believe that the work capacity of draft animals is also reduced. Naturally, this would be serious in lands which must rely upon animals as a source of power for some time to come.

Of equal importance with low levels of material production, are low fertility, increased mortality of the young, and slow development to reproductive maturity.

Table 9

ESTIMATED WOOL PRODUCTION OF SHEEP IN
SELECTED COUNTRIES, 1953-54 (13e, 1955)

Country	Thousands of animals	Thousands of metric tons (clean wool)	Average production per animal (kilos)
Australia	126,944	327	2.58
United States	31,861[1]	61	1.91
Argentina	55,500[2]	96	1.73
Union of South Africa	35,992	61	1.69
United Kingdom	22,873[1]	32	1.40
Spain	20,000[3]	26	1.30
France	7,826	10	1.28
Syria	3,746	4	1.07
Brazil	16,800	15	.89
Colombia	1,341	1	.75
Libya	1,433	1	.70
Algeria	6,014	4	.67
India	36,830	18	.49
French Morocco	13,556[4]	6	.44

Note: Figures are for 1953-54 except Colombia, French Morocco and Union of South Africa which are for 1952-53; Libya, 1951-52; and India, 1948-52 average.

[1] In agricultural holdings only.
[2] Unofficial figure.
[3] Animals over one year old.
[4] Animals registered for taxation.

THE EFFECTS OF CLIMATE

While it is true that the statistics upon which any one of the foregoing tables is based are open to some question, the concentration of tropical countries toward the bottom of each table warrants the conclusion that animal production in the tropics is indeed at a low level. The question arises, however, as to the extent that this is attributable to climate per se.

The ways in which climate may affect domestic animals are even more complex than those affecting plants, and an over-all assessment is correspondingly more difficult to make.

For the purposes of discussion it is usually necessary to consider the various aspects one at a time, but the interaction between the various effects must be remembered, and a final judgment in any particular case should be made only in terms of the full range of possible effects.

Through Nutrition

From what has been said in the chapter on crop production, it should not come as a surprise to find that tropical grasses and other forage plants, even when abundant, are frequently lacking in nutritive value. In many instances, poor nutrition constitutes a major cause of low animal productivity in the tropics (13b). Lands which experience long periods of scanty rainfall, especially if these occur in the hot season, cannot be expected to support high levels of production. Table 10, for example, illustrates the intimate relationship between rainfall and the grazing capacity of range land in the United States.

Table 10

GRAZING CAPACITY OF U.S. RANGE LAND IN RELATION TO AVERAGE ANNUAL PRECIPITATION (49b)

Average annual precipitation (inches)	Acres required to support cow for year	
	Range in good condition	Range in average condition
5-10	60-200	200 or more
10-15	35-80	70-200
15-20	25-45	40-120
20-25	12-35	15-50
25-30	8-15	10-40
over 30	3-12	3-20

In regions with long periods of hot, rainy weather, on the other hand, the temperature and precipitation combine to leach the soils of soluble minerals and nitrogenous compounds, leaving the vegetation poor in those constituents which are so essential to the nourishment of animals. The lush growth, which the word "tropics" evokes in the minds of many people, is deceptive indeed. As was pointed out in Chapter 3, the natural vegetation remains lush only so long as it is left alone. In the second place, its bulk is largely composed of water (of which the animal has an abundance) and of fibre (which is poorly digestible and heat-provoking). Protein, which is so important to the animal, is usually in low concentration, and digestible carbohydrates are relatively deficient. This is well brought out in Table 11, although it must be remembered that the nutritive contents of herbage vary, not only with the species and the climate, but also with the method of management and the stage of development.

Table 11

PERCENTAGE OF DRY MATTER, DIGESTIBLE CRUDE PROTEIN, AND STARCH EQUIVALENT CONTAINED IN 100 POUNDS OF GREEN GRASS (41)

Forage	Dry matter	Digestible crude protein	Starch equivalent
Coarse grasses of Trinidad:			
Elephant	19.8	0.9	8.1
Guatemala	20.4	1.3	7.9
Uba cane	23.4	1.4	11.9
Bamboo grass	20.8	0.6	7.7
United Kingdom pasture:			
Closely grazed, 3 week rotation	20.0	3.7	14.6
Closely grazed, 4 week rotation	20.0	2.6	13.4
Extensively grazed, average	20.0	2.2	11.3

It has been estimated that a 1,000-lb. dairy cow would need to eat nearly 66 lbs. of such elephant grass per day to obtain her requirements of digestible crude protein for maintenance, and nearly 100 lbs. to obtain her maintenance requirements for total digestible nutrients.

In addition to the simple undernutrition which results from dependence upon poor forage, animals may suffer from bone maladies, anemia, goiter, and numerous ill-defined disturbances as a result of inadequate or ill-balanced supplies of both major minerals (calcium, phosphate) and trace elements (cobalt, manganese, iodine, etc.).

When the available nutrients are scanty and competition

for them is keen, the small animal, having a lower daily requirement for survival, has a certain advantage over the larger one. Quite possibly, this has led over long periods of time to the natural selection of smaller animals and the elimination of larger ones, with the resulting preponderance of small animals seen today, for example, among the cattle of Ceylon and Bengal. Unfortunately, the same selection pressure works against the type of animals desired by man; i.e. animals which produce more milk than is absolutely necessary for the survival of calves, animals which develop a more edible carcass, or evolve a body form adapted to more work than is essential to self-preservation. On the other hand, the highly selected small animals are likely to have a ruggedness which makes them better adapted to strenuous conditions than animals developed under more advantageous circumstances.

Through Disease

Although it would be hard to prove that any one particular disease is necessarily confined to tropical regions, it is undoubtedly true that certain ones are more commonly seen there than elsewhere. In part, this may be due to poorer management, as is indicated by the prevalence of bovine tuberculosis, brucellosis, and foot and mouth disease, which can appear nearly anywhere that cattle are maintained without proper precautions. Just as with the ailments affecting man and plants, however, the prevalence of many animal diseases is undoubtedly aided by warm and humid conditions. This is particularly true of those caused by parasites hatching from eggs in the soil or transmitted by insects, such as the trypanosomiases. The absence of killing frosts, a virtually guaranteed optimum relative humidity, and an abundance of nutrient material, all provide an ideal medium for the growth and multiplication of organism, vector (i.e. disease carrier) and immune reservoir host alike.

The names anaplasmosis, piroplasmosis, ngana, surra, liver fluke, hydatid, fly strike, and helminthiasis, all too familiar to animal producers in the tropics, proclaim the extent and economic importance of animal diseases occurring in the hotter regions of the earth. As was pointed out in the preceding chapter, the ecological pattern of the humid tropics is that of a multiplicity of species, constant competition, and continuous evolutionary experiment. In such a milieu every opportunity is given for the emergence of some inimical agent whenever a new species or strain of domestic animal is introduced. Man has achieved some notable victories in his campaign against tropical diseases, but the guerrilla tactics of nature in the tropics are not easily overcome, and victory in one phase may be largely offset by new disease developments in another.

The following extracts from the *Proceedings* of the United Nations Scientific Conference on the Conservation and Utilization of Resources (48d) will indicate the significance of certain diseases of livestock in tropical regions.

A person whose experience of [foot-and-mouth] disease is confined to temperate climates can scarcely appreciate to the full the devastating losses caused by it [in the Indo-Pakistan subcontinent]. Points requiring special mention are its extremely wide prevalence, its tendency to occur at inopportune moments, e.g., in the Punjab about May-June at the time when cattle are required for threshing, and its frequently serious sequelae. Among the latter may be mentioned myiasis of the foot with consequent slow healing and often sloughing of the hoof, and the condition known as "panting," a permanent derangement of the heat-regulatory system. Panting is especially common in imported European and their cross-bred stock on the military farms. Again on these same farms, the foot lesions in a heavy bull may be so severe and enduring that the animal is incapable of serving, with the result that the breeding stops and the whole routine is upset.

. . . . .

Anthrax is widespread in hot moist areas like Malabar, Madras, Orissa, and Bengal because the atmospheric conditions there are highly favourable for sporulation of the organism. Such areas constitute permanently infected foci, from which the disease is carried to temperate countries through infected skins, etc.

Rinderpest is a highly fatal devastating disease of ruminating animals endemic in oriental countries, India and Africa, but does not exist in the Western Hemisphere. Sudden appearing outbreaks in water buffalo may result in sufficient mortality to seriously interfere with rice culture, and thereby human food supply.

Internal parasites cause severe losses among all classes of farm animals. Despite the fact that they are responsible for some of the worst diseases, they cause their heaviest losses by an unspectacular, insidious undermining of the health of millions of animals.

. . . . .

In cattle, several protozoan diseases are as important as the major helminthic diseases. In large areas of the world, trypanosomes and piroplasms are serious hazards in cattle production. In Africa, for example, the effective control of bovine trypanosomiasis would remove a major obstacle to successful cattle raising and permit almost limitless expansion of an immeasurably profitable and crucially needed livestock industry.

. . . . .

Mention might well be made . . . of the occurrence of the liver fluke in certain tropical areas. In Hawaii, for example, it infects 80 per cent of the dairy cattle and 50 per cent of the beef animals. One group of 419 dairy cows slaughtered on Oahu in 1939 revealed 91.8 per cent with fluky livers. Another parasite, Oesophagostomum radiatum, has been shown to be one of the causes of so-called "tropical diarrhoea" of calves in Puerto Rico. The parasite causes anaemia, stunting, and other serious symptoms. The daily gains of infected calves were found to be only about one-seventh of the gains of uninfected controls.

Through Direct Action on Animals

When exposed to heat, domesticated animals increase their breathing in an attempt to increase the rate of heat loss by evaporation. In spite of this, however, the body temperature is very likely to rise, to an extent determined by the severity of the external conditions, the productive level of the animal, and its type. A number of undesirable consequences ensue, partly as a result of the increased breathing, partly from the rise of body temperature, and partly from further adjustments in the secretions of the ductless glands.

The rapid breathing interferes with eating and even with rumination; it tends to upset the balance between acidic and basic substances in the blood stream; and itself increases the work and heat production of the animal. Appetite is lost, and if the animal is on open pasture it may lie down or seek shade in preference to eating. If this occurs where the nutritive value of the pasture is low, it may be impossible for the animal to make up in the cooler hours what it loses by inanition in the hotter parts of the day. The animal therefore tends to be less well nourished than it would otherwise be; milk production, growth, work capacity, and other types of productivity suffer; and fertility may be seriously reduced. These direct affects of hot climates correspond very closely with the types of disturbance mentioned at the beginning of the chapter, and might account almost entirely for those disturbances in certain limited localities. In most instances, however, they are reinforced by the indirect effects of climate through malnutrition and disease.

So prevalent are the indirect nutritional and infective consequences that it is difficult to determine in the field what may be the direct effect of climate upon the physiological well-being of livestock. The importance of these two factors, whether themselves due to climate or not, has been appreciated for a long time, and extensive investigations have been conducted in many different parts of the world in an attempt to understand them and control their ill-effects. The specific study of direct climatic effects is, by contrast, quite recent. Sporadic attempts have been made for fifty years, or more, to identify these direct effects and determine their mode of operation, but the effort has become systematic only in the last ten years, as the techniques applied to the study of human reactions to the full range of climatic stresses encountered in World War II have been applied to animal problems. As the indirect operations of climate through poor nutrition and disease become better understood, its direct action emerges more clearly. Moreover, as the indirect effects come under control, the direct effects become proportionately more important. When cattle are decimated by foot-and-mouth disease, the "comfort" of the animal is of little importance; but when, in the absence of disease and malnutrition, cattle can develop their productive potential, the depressive effects of hot conditions acquire greater economic significance.

These studies proceed through the usual three phases of any scientific investigation of practical problems. Preliminary evidence is collected in the field where the problem arises, but the circumstances there are too complex to permit definite conclusions. Laboratory studies are then instituted in order to isolate the variables and to study each without confusion by the others. As knowledge emerges from these detailed procedures, ideas must be taken back to the field and re-examined under natural conditions, and further evidence collected in the light of the laboratory experience. By continual comparison of the natural but complex field evidence with the more precise but "artificial" laboratory findings, a picture of the underlying processes is built up and a rational solution to the problems approached. Ten years of systematic study have yielded such a partial picture, the outlines of which are decidedly relevant to the considerations of this chapter.

There is no doubt that the ability of animals to withstand tropical conditions can vary considerably between different types and breeds. For example, field observation and laboratory experiment show that the humped Indian (zebu) cattle usually show a markedly greater heat tolerance than do most European cattle; that the White Leghorn hen has a greater heat tolerance than many other breeds of chicken; and that Merino and Corriedale sheep can stand hot conditions better than most "Downs" breeds. As among European dairy cattle, Jerseys bear heat better than Holsteins.

This type of information is of direct practical importance, but a survey undertaken for the Food and Agriculture Organization under the author's direction reveals that it is far from systematic. Few comparisons have been made between animals under identical or comparable conditions. Varying levels of production in the animals compared and different nutritional levels have frequently confused findings. Furthermore, the criteria used in making comparisons tend to vary from one group of observers to another. Much needs to be done before anything like a systematic catalog of comparative tolerances toward hot conditions can be compiled.

For a proper understanding of the problem and for a rational as opposed to an empirical solution, it is necessary to know not only whether an individual animal, a type, or a breed is more tolerant of heat than another, but *why* it is more tolerant. If it can be shown just what qualities confer high heat tolerance upon an individual, breeders could be guided more precisely than is now possible in selecting animals with better tolerance. In some cases this would seem to be associated with the circumstances of the individual—heavily fed animals, and particularly very fat animals, often show a lower heat tolerance. But in many cases the difference seems to be genetic rather than nutritional.

This field of study is in its infancy, but the idea is emerging that an important difference lies in the animal's "efficiency," that is, its ability to convert food energy into useful products like milk, meat, or work, with minimal production of heat. A cow which produces 30 lbs. of milk, representing 10,000 calories of energy from food containing 13,000 calories of available energy, liberating only 3,000 calories of heat in the process, will be a more desirable animal than one which requires 15,000 calories in food and liberates 5,000 calories as heat. Because it is a more efficient converter of its own food into milk, it gets less hot in the process; because it gets less hot in the process, it is less likely to suffer from the effects of hot conditions. It thus has a double advantage under hot conditions over the less efficient animals. To the farmer it will have the added attraction of eating less food— or producing more milk for the same food.

What must be realized, however, is that everything man asks of his animals—more meat, more milk, more eggs, more work—involves a greater production of heat. He must be prepared to compromise with nature at a level of production somewhat less than that obtainable in temperate zones. Studies made by the author and his colleagues tend to discount the more popular beliefs that one animal sweats more than another, or that appendages such as the dewlap of Indian cattle are special heat exchangers.

Human beings have long accepted the fact that, as far as their own reactions are concerned, humidity is as important as high temperatures. To a certain extent this seems to be true for domesticated animals as well, but there is reason to believe that the relative importance of the two is somewhat different for them. As will be seen in Chapter 5, enough work has been done on man for the relative importance of these two factors to him to be fairly well mapped out, but similar studies have been made only infrequently on animals. Until this is done, it is difficult to predict what the effect of a given temperature–humidity combination will be upon a given type of animal.

An environmental factor which seems to have only a minor effect upon man, but which may markedly complicate an animal's efficiency, is the amount of daylight. The reproductive cycle in many wild animals is closely linked in temperate and cold regions to the seasonal variation in hours of daylight, and there is reason to believe that this is likewise of some consequence to domesticated animals (39). When animals are moved from intermediate to low latitudes, the seasonal variation is markedly diminished, and perhaps reversed. Some evidence shows that this may help to upset the reproductive function.

On Storage and Handling of Products

The possible range of effects of tropical climates upon animal products is certainly no less restricted than that upon plant products discussed in Chapter 3. As compared with meat, milk, butter, and eggs, such plant products as cereals and legumes might be considered almost stable and resistant. Some form of preservation is essential unless these animal foods are to be consumed immediately after production. The high environmental temperatures speed up natural deteriorative reactions. Microorganisms abound in the moist conditions, which permeate everything that is not sealed in a dry state. Insects and rodents will invade or break through all but the toughest or specially treated containers.

The danger of disease is bad enough, but the esthetic effects are perhaps, in the end, more influential. Only those who have regularly had to face half-melted and partially rancid butter swimming in its own oily exudate, or cheese sweating in the middle but curled up like discarded leather at the edges, can appreciate the dampening effect that unprotected products can have upon an appetite already somewhat less than normal. The difficulties created by these hazards, and the expense of adequate safeguards, undoubtedly have a lot to do with the low consumption of animal products in many tropical areas and act as a deterrent to rapid expansion of animal industry.

CIRCUMVENTING THE EFFECTS

As with plant production, tropical climates impose difficulties on animal production, but there is every reason to suppose that the future looms much brighter than the past. In some respects the fact that scientific attention to animal production lags behind that given to plant production is an encouragement. The advances made in plant science serve as a challenge to animal research. To a certain extent also, plant improvement should precede animal improvement, since the full capabilities of various types of animal cannot be revealed, or peculiarly animal problems clearly seen, until full nourishment can be secured for them.

Improved Nutrition

Undoubtedly much could be done to improve the productivity of tropical livestock simply by improving the nutritional quality, as well as the quantity, of feed they receive. Additional cultivation, or even the replacement of natural herbage by better species, can greatly increase the nutritive supplies, provided that the selected plant types are adaptable to prevailing conditions and conserve the soil. In a list of 37 types of forage covering 22 species used in Brazil, 10 are shown as containing over 10 per cent of crude protein (13b). The regulation of grazing so that rank growth is kept down but overgrazing avoided, can usually be counted upon to step up the concentration of nutrients (see Table 11). The development of new forage types by experimental breeding is constantly extending the opportunity for improving land which formerly provided poor grazing. Pasture improvement is rapidly advancing as the importance of controlled clearing, soil conservation, and the application of fertilizers comes to be appreciated. Where the soil, and consequently forage, is deficient in certain trace elements, great improvement can sometimes be effected by simply applying them on the ground.

These things are known, and fresh advances are regularly being made, but their application tends to lag for a variety of reasons which will be considered shortly. Suffice it to say for the moment that there is cause for at least restrained optimism.

Disease Control

To say that the control of infectious disease is improving at the same spectacular rate with animals as it seems to be with humans would probably be an exaggeration; but undoubtedly much of what is learned in the realm of human infection has its relevance for veterinary medicine. The problem of vector eradication, as well as of animal medication, is made formidable by the vast areas over which domesticated animals range and the infrequent handling of many types. Reservoirs of infection among wild animals are even more difficult to treat than similar reservoirs in human populations. Nevertheless, dipping and spraying animals to kill ticks and other ectoparasites, vaccination, injection of suppressives, rigid control of slaughtered carcasses, and quarantine, are having their effect. It is not too much to hope that some of the more important diseases are on their way to elimination from certain tropical areas, in the way that piroplasmosis was eliminated from Texas. At the same time, rotational herd management and anthelminthics are reducing the intensity of worm infestation, if not the number of affected animals, so that the productivity of the herd is less restricted by this indirect climatic effect.

Breeding

The highly developed domestic animals in most temperate countries today have been selectively bred from much less attractive progenitors over longer or shorter periods of time. This process is continuing with sufficiently frequent additions to the catalog of effective animals to give the impression that breeding is the most promising answer to many problems of animal production (39). The surest way of improving tropical livestock, it seems, would be by breeding animals adapted to the environment. Even a casual glance at the existing livestock of many tropical countries will disclose their heterogeneous nature, and increase the expectation of results to be obtained by selective breeding.

While it is true that much can be done by concentrating the genes for high production through an intensive program of selective breeding, the limitations of such a program must also be borne in mind. In the first place, any such program is necessarily slow. With animals such as poultry, which come to reproductive maturity fairly quickly, generations may follow rapidly enough for success to be reasonably certain. With slow maturing animals like cattle, a long time must elapse before the worth of a particular program can be seen. The occasional relatively quick success, such as the development of the Santa Gertrudis breed of beef cattle (39), must not be allowed to obscure the more usual indecisive result. Furthermore, any long-term plan presupposes continuity of direction and purpose—a continuity which was tenuous enough in the Western world which developed modern breeds, but which is wholly wanting even today in many of the areas seeking animal improvement.

But more serious than either of these limitations are the physiological conflicts between improved production and certain consequences of that improvement. More milk, more meat, more eggs, or more wool all mean more heat liberation, and this in a climate where heat is often a burden, and sometimes a critical one. (Albert Rhoad, however, feels that this is not so true for meat animals.) Moreover, increased production will call for greater food consumption, unless the increased production comes about by an improvement in the conversion efficiency of the animal (i.e., the conversion of a greater proportion of the original feed energy into useful products). In many regions feed is insufficient for present production, and any increased production predicated on more feed is necessarily illusory. But if more efficient animals (in the conversion of energy) are used, greater production could result from the same consumption of food.

Selective breeding, therefore, could effect an improvement in animal production, but it is likely to be slow, uncertain, expensive, and by no means the main route to a golden future. In a paper prepared for the Study Group's conference, Rhoad advocated a greater emphasis upon the improvement of environment (including nutrition and prevention of disease) than upon breeding, and in breeding, equal emphasis upon resistance to the environment as upon production per se. As between different classes of livestock he had this to say:

Undoubtedly the meat animals, swine and beef cattle, especially the latter, can be brought into higher and more efficient production quicker (on a national economy basis) than the dairy cow and the hen.

The reasons for placing beef production at the top of this scale are several. What they consume, herbage, is generally abundant in the tropics; they occupy the more remote cheaper lands, the deficiencies of which may be corrected through small quantities of cheap supplements (usually minerals). Heritability of production is high; and because this is expressed in both sexes, genetic improvement through mass selection is relatively rapid. Beef is the cheapest animal product in the diet of tropical peoples.

Pork production may be rapidly increased through adequate management of the young. Production, however, is largely limited by food supply. Because the pig competes with humans for the same basic foods, cereals and animal protein, always apparently in low supply in the tropics, the adequate feeding of pigs is usually expensive. The hog for the most part is still the scavenger around the farm. Pork is expensive, usually twice or more the price of beef in the American tropics. It is the meat of special occasions.

The development of a superior breed of tropical dairy cattle is one of the most challenging and urgent problems confronting the animal husbandman in the warmer climates. It is complicated because only a few of the tropical indigenous or so-called native breeds are as efficient producers of milk as they are of beef. Because of this, resort to crossbreeding with the specialized dairy breeds has been carried on far more extensively and haphazardly than with the beef breeds. The development of tropical dairy breeds is receiving special attention in many areas, advancements have been made, but the industry still lacks a dairy breed that can be used for grading-up the common stock for increased milk production, retaining with it adaptability to tropical conditions. . . .

I place the poultry industry at the bottom of this scale, not because production cannot be rapidly increased through good management, but because of the cost factor, especially for feed. Farm and backyard flocks are the rule in the tropics with birds scratching a living as they can, supplemented with table scraps. To place large numbers together restricted in their range requires balanced rations of the most complicated mixtures known in animal husbandry. These, ready mixed or their ingredients for home mixing, are uncertain in supply and very expensive when available. In only a few centers in the American tropics are conditions satisfactory for the development of modern poultry industry. An adequate source of feed is the major limiting factor. Eggs and poultry meat are almost luxury items in the diet when they must be purchased on the market.

(It should be pointed out that somewhat different views are held by others, and that the economic expediency of swine and poultry raising is affected by the cultural habits of the population. But the views expressed here have considerable validity in many areas.)

Management

As Samuel Work pointed out, climate and environment do not constitute the whole reason for differences in production between countries. Bland Cuba has twice as many cattle per capita as rugged Iceland, but only one-fourth the quantity of milk. In Nicaragua, on the other hand, the ratio of cattle to population is similar to that in Cuba, but the milk supply is twice as great. Variations are due, in part, to differences in the productive capacities of the cattle maintained; yet, even within a country with one type of cattle, vast differences in the results are obtained by different owners. European-type cattle can be kept up to high productive levels in certain Caribbean and Central American localities by careful management. Instances were cited of cows giving 40 lbs. per day in Nicaragua, 25 lbs. per day in Honduras,

Table 12

AVERAGE PRODUCTION OF MILK (lbs./day) IN EL SALVADOR

Month	Pure-blood Holstein & Brown-Swiss	Crosses	Criollos with concentrate	Criollos without concentrate	All cows
November 1953	25.60	12.71	9.66	7.18	11.17
December	29.09	12.07	9.37	6.72	11.90
January 1954	27.98	12.35	10.38	7.05	12.61
February	26.99	14.23	10.45	7.34	13.02
March	27.26	14.50	11.04	8.34	13.66
April	26.60	13.95	9.38	9.59	13.09
May	24.97	13.76	11.28	9.40	13.42
June	25.00	13.93	10.64	8.15	12.96
July	23.18	14.08	10.81	7.61	12.57
August	23.06	14.92	11.34	8.58	13.39
September	21.80	14.47	11.36	6.40	12.10
October	22.56	14.53	10.78	6.83	12.76
Year	25.25	13.87	10.54	7.81	12.87

Source: Information supplied by L. Escalón for Third FAO Meeting on Livestock Production in the Americas, 1955.

and even 70 lbs. per day in El Salvador. Table 12 gives some interesting data from last-named country.

The way of the husbandman in tropical regions may not be harassed by the blizzard, but in its stead innumerable forces work quietly and incessantly to return to the jungle that which man seeks to wrest from it. Far from being able to rely upon a kindly nature to repay an initial courtship with "natural increase" and maintained yield, the producer must constantly be on his guard against deterioration and continually seek better ways to adapt the principles of his craft to the strange and subtle ways of tropical ecology. As in plant production, and as in all other aspects of human endeavor, success in the tropics comes not to the man who would escape responsibilities and rely upon natural abundance, but to the one who will plan and work as hard or harder than his counterpart in temperate climes. The rewards can be won, but only by those who have and are prepared to give what it takes.

From the increasing store of knowledge of the ways in which tropical environments affect domestic animals, whether directly through physiological reactions or indirectly through malnutrition and disease, the producer can gather suggestions for protecting his animals or assisting them to meet the stresses. Providing shade, for example, is a simple, but frequently neglected measure, which can be taken by conserving suitable trees, or by erecting simple and cheap shelters. Barns for stud animals or milking cows can be designed so that the roof is shaded, and air movement maintained throughout to remove heat and moisture as fast as it is developed. Careful records can be kept to reveal the less profitable animals that should be culled and the conditions of management that bring better returns. Simple but regular inspection of animals and the conditions under which they are maintained, when carried out by a man who understands the nature of the many-sided problem and is constantly looking for ways to anticipate dangers, can be most effective. It is not merely in human medicine that "more mistakes are made by not looking than by not knowing." Alert men gain support from advances in science and technology, and at the same time contribute to the advance of knowledge. If a majority of the tropical producers would emulate those few who are already taking advantage of their opportunities, optimism for the future need not be so restrained.

COMPLICATING FACTORS

As with crop production, it is important to recognize certain nonclimatic difficulties in meeting climatic stress. In the breeding and use of animals, man seems to have created even more than the usual quota of difficulties for himself. Problems of land tenure, which so often interfere with the judicious production of crops, are likely to have an even greater effect upon animal husbandry, since so much more land and capital are required. If it is difficult for the small tenant farmer or sharecropper to establish his independence, it is virtually impossible for the herdsman to escape from servitude under a system where ownership is in the hands of a few. In addition to this restraint animal industry in the tropics has nonclimatic problems of its own.

Social Restraints

Western countries are given to joking about the peculiar and conservative eating habits of each other, but these habits are no more than passing whimsies when seen against the centuries- or even millennia-old customs of many tropical peoples. Today's fare in many Middle Eastern localities differs little from Biblical times. The native diets of Polynesians seem to have changed but little from those of their migrating ancestors more than two thousand years ago. In these age-old habits animal food has a small and usually well-defined place, not easily influenced by the alien modern world. Moreover, in their own setting these people do not feel that their diets are deficient; and toward outsiders who urge a change they are likely to display more resentment than concurrence. If it were possible for them to remain in isolation, living out their own lives in their own way, we would have to respect their preferences, and an argument for increased animal production would have little force. But if we accept the view that these peoples will inevitably be caught up in world affairs and be forced to compete on terms not their own, then we have a case for pressing improved nutrition upon them, and with it an increased dependence on animal products.

Social resistance gains greater force when it is formalized in taboos or religious prohibitions. To all those of Hindu faith, except perhaps a few radicals, the cow, as the mother of the human race, is sacrosanct. To the Moslem, consumption of pig meat is just as abhorrent, though for a different reason. The Masai inhabitants of the Rift Valley reverse the proscription by permitting warriors to eat meat and drink blood, while forbidding them any vegetables; but in neighboring tribes, almost the sole purpose of cattle is to serve as tokens of prestige. To attempt conversion by argument, as by pointing out that the hygenic or conservationist origin of the proscription has long ago lost its force, would be as foolish as it would be useless. These restrictions must be accepted until time and understanding have softened the resistance.

A matter of more immediate significance, in that something might be done to change it, is the traditional separation in many tropical countries of those who are planners and scholars from those who labor. Scholarship and executive power are handicapped in working for the common good if they are never tempered by personal experience of the actualities of labor. Labor, on the other hand, loses many opportunities for advancing technology and productivity if it remains untutored. The dignity of labor is still a novel and untested idea in many of the tropical countries with a traditional attitude toward social organization. Indeed, in many this respect for tradition has been fostered until recently by the temperate powers who have been controlling their destinies. In the desire for change which is abroad today the more extreme attitudes may be broken down, but the inertia of tradition, and the attachment to older forms which paradoxically tends to accompany an upsurge of nationalism, may retard the process. It is to be hoped, however, that progress in this respect will be made, since without a close liaison between thought and practice, real improvement in animal husbandry will be seriously impeded.

Poor Economic Incentive

A country in which the agricultural returns are meager in proportion to the population, and other products are insufficient to pay for imported supplements, finds itself committed to what might be called a "land-to-mouth" existence. Even when crops are conveyed directly to human mouths, little more than mere existence is possible, and there appears to be little scope for the energetically wasteful process of first feeding crops to animals and then using animal products for food. Animals tend to be admitted or maintained in the economy only to the extent that they are essential sources of power or means of distribution, and then only on a precarious basis.

The community finds itself struggling to maintain an equilibrium at the lowest level; movement to a higher level is beyond the imagination of the individual peasant, except through some form of divine intervention. To such a peasant there is no economic incentive to increased animal husbandry, at least until his crop returns have been put on a much sounder basis, or the national economy recast in an entirely different pattern by an agency beyond his ken. There can be few forms of conservatism more deeply rooted than that of a man who has everything to lose and very little hope of anything to gain by experiment or change.

To the extent that animals already form part of a regional farm economy, there is a case for improvement; but the farmer may ask, as an Indian peasant asked me, what he would do with the increased product. If his draft animals worked more and helped him to grow more crops, what would he do with the surplus? Already he may well have enough crops for his own use, but a marked need of other foods that he does not grow himself. In other words, for an increase in production to be effective, a simultaneous improvement in the means of distribution and exchange may be necessary. The argument that increased production, especially by the indirect method of animal improvement, would be of direct benefit to the farmer breaks down unless he can see quite clearly just how a surplus in his crop can be exchanged for things which he needs.

The difficulties placed by tropical climates in the way of efficient distribution and exchange—spoilage, interruption to transportation, destruction—have already been mentioned in relation to both plant and animal products. In each case they reinforce the skepticism of the farmer, especially the very poor one, about the supposed benefits of increased production. And it must be admitted that this skepticism is often more difficult to counter in the matter of animal than in plant production.

Ignorance

The self-perpetuating triad of conservatism, ignorance, and poverty is at least as influential in animal husbandry as in crop production. Methods of management which have persisted over centuries have one thing in their favor—they must have been moderately successful, and the traditional farmer will not be slow to point this out. Nevertheless, the essential question is, will those methods continue to be adequate under the conditions and demands of today or might not the application of present knowledge give still better results? The peasant farmer in regions somewhat isolated from the current of world events is apt to be ill-informed on these points, or even unaware of the question. It is difficult to see how this could be otherwise in countries with little if any provision for rural education. Indeed, comparable ignorance is not unknown in countries with much more extensive and advanced educational practices. Certainly the cooperation of the individual farmer in improvement programs must remain uncertain until a larger measure of education is possible than exists today.

Education for improving tropical animal husbandry encounters two difficulties. The first lies in presenting the idea that a certain balance between plant and animal production is necessary for national development. In spite of the clamor of the few, the concept of national welfare is probably still strange to peasant farmers who for centuries have had little knowledge of or concern for the world beyond their immediate neighborhood. If it is difficult to convince them that balanced animal and crop farming is in their own immediate interest, an appeal to the vague concept of national welfare is unlikely to be any more successful. The second difficulty arises where animal production has been carried on for a long time on a family basis, each family owning a few animals. Improvement here probably calls for consolidating animals into larger holdings managed by organized groups. This conversion "from backyard to stockyard" necessitates both a profound change in mental outlook and the development of an economic and technical maturity that is strange to the loosely knit traditional structure. Acceptance cannot be expected overnight. Indeed, too rapid an acceptance might be a sign of instability and a grasping at straws, rather than the desired maturity.

REQUIRED ACTION

Tropical climates undoubtedly interfere, directly and indirectly, with animal production. Some of this interference can be countered by applying present knowledge; on the other hand, there are influential nonclimatic complications. While crop production urgently calls for action in a majority of underdeveloped tropical areas, in many of them animal production is almost equally deserving of immediate attention. Since most domestic animals have a longer breeding cycle than crop plants, improvement comes about much more slowly and requires a proportionately greater investment of capital. For this reason, an early start and deliberate planning are particularly necessary in animal industry. But it must be remembered that for physiological reasons, the maximum productive levels to be expected of animals in the tropics lie somewhat below those found under the best circumstances in temperate zones. Desirable procedures may again be considered under the headings of management, research, and education, although in practice action must usually be compounded of all three.

Management

Standards of animal husbandry leave much to be desired in many parts of the tropics and subtropics, and considerable improvement in returns could be expected from a simple improvement of those standards. Greater attention to the simple and almost universal principles of animal care—avoidance of overstocking, rotation of pastures, conservation of shade trees, culling of undesirables, control of predators, provision of watering points, assistance in adverse seasons—is badly needed, and prerequisite to the success of the more specific and more widely advertised measures of pasture improvement, disease prevention, and breeding.

The introduction of new and more nutritious pasture plants is undoubtedly important and should be encouraged; but the suitability of a type for a particular location must first be established and the cost of introduction examined. Sound conservation practices must also be instituted to prevent erosion and leaching of the soil, and grazing should be so arranged that it encourages new growth without endangering the plant. Overstocking must be rigidly curtailed. Where they are deficient, trace elements should be added to the soil or supplied in licks, and consideration may have to be given to the application of soluble minerals or nitrogenous compounds. There is little point in applying fertilizers, however, if they will simply be swept away in run-off or seepage. The use of fertilizers must be part of a well-designed plan to get nutrients into a soil-plant cycle which will maintain them in situ with no more than relatively minor periodical supplements. Conservation practices such as these may well bring about improvement even in native pastures and make the introduction of new types less urgent, or provide the sorely needed capital for such introductions through the increased returns.

Preventive inoculation against those diseases for which it is effective is certainly desirable, but the system of management may need modification to make the animals available for treatment. Medication may be economically justifiable in a small concentrated herd; it is difficult to apply to larger or more scattered groups. Control of infective agents by means appropriate to the particular agent and the circumstances of management must always be considered, but many difficulties may be encountered. Disease carriers may be discouraged by insecticides sprayed on barns or on the animals, or controlled at the breeding sites. Animals may be protected against vectors by screening or limitation to clean areas. Nondomestic animals acting as reservoirs of infection may be quarantined or eliminated. Rotation of pastures helps to restrict worm infestation. Producer cooperation may be enforced by a rigid system of product inspection or slaughter of infected animals. But all these measures are costly and by no means fool-proof. In some regions they may be pushed to the point of virtually eradicating certain diseases; in others public apathy or prohibitive costs may interfere with tangible improvement.

Much could be done by simple selection of superior stock and elimination of inferior stock in those areas where selective breeding has not been practiced. Again, limitations to such a simple plan will be encountered as time goes on. The rate of progress must diminish as desirable genes become concentrated, and more exact definitions of desirable characteristics must be formulated when the obvious differences between the best and the worst have been reduced. Practical breeding then becomes increasingly dependent upon research and planned experiment, a procedure which is apt to be both sophisticated and costly for an underdeveloped country. Selection, it cannot be overemphasized, must be directed toward the particular circumstances of climate, nutrition, and management that the animals must face. A type well adapted to the conditions of the Gulf Coast may not be suitable for Cuba or the Amazon Basin. Again, it may be possible to speed up the concentration of desirable genes in some groups by crossing with breeds imported from elsewhere, though in some areas the local animals have as much to offer. Improvement by breeding will be facilitated if careful records are kept and subjected to continual examination; and it will be still further facilitated if only proven sires are used. The practice of artificial insemination may be used to obtain maximum effectiveness of proven sires. On the matter of breeding for heat tolerance, I have had occasion to advise against any attempt to select animals for hot conditions on the basis of morphological characters (13c). Instead, more emphasis should be placed upon selecting those animals which show smaller rises of temperature when exposed to hot conditions, show less urge to seek shade or stop eating on hot days, or show a greater conversion ratio of fodder to product when studied in the test barn—i.e., animals with greater efficiency, irrespective of external characters.

Research

Our knowledge of existing pasture plants is far from complete. In many instances the characteristics of a plant are known only in its native habitat, so that its suitability for another situation is largely a matter of guesswork. Much work needs to be done, first to establish the physiological requirements of known pasture plants, and then to determine how these might be provided in a different situation. With the progress of plant genetics the prospect of developing new types is rapidly expanding, and with it the possibility of securing pasture plants more suited to the special and often difficult situations under which it is desirable to maintain livestock. Where fodder must be stored against poor seasons or transported to concentrated groups of animals, the further problem arises of selecting or developing plants which will lend themselves to such practices without serious loss of nutritive value.

While the main course of infectious disease is now fairly well known, many aspects remain which are imperfectly understood. This is particularly true with diseases caused by viruses, and it applies also to such problems as the host-parasite relationship. We do not know, for example, why ticks attach themselves readily to European-type cattle, but leave

Indian-type cattle much less infested. There are still many problems of immunity and epidemiology, moreover, whose solutions would greatly help in the preservation of animal health.

As with plant production, genetics is one field of research which seems to be particularly relevant to problems of animal industry in the tropics. Very little indeed is known about the genetics of heat tolerance, resistance to disease, or efficient utilization of feed. Practically nothing is known of the genetic potentialities of indigenous tropical animals. Until far more information is gained about these matters and a much better understanding is established, breeding practices must continue in their present empirical and groping fashion, guided only by statistical analysis of past results.

But genetic studies of this kind cannot be conducted in isolation. The traits desired by the producers are very largely of a physiological order—resistance, efficiency, production—on which information is by no means adequate. In the ten years of systematic study of direct climatic effects, no more than an outline of the mechanisms involved has been obtained. Although the present activity makes a noticeable ripple in the quiet pool of ignorance, the resultant effect is still small. Much more effort and extensive study is required before specific advice can be given to animal industry with any great degree of confidence. Even in the field of animal nutrition, which has been organized much longer, considerable doubt and uncertainty remain, especially when one attempts to apply general principles to the special circumstances of the tropics.

For a better understanding of environmental effects upon animals both laboratory and field studies are needed. While some of the basic investigation can be carried out in temperate centers, it must be supported and extended by systematic inquiry in the tropics. A small number of well-equipped laboratories, situated at strategic points throughout the tropics, with field observations carried out in co-ordinated fashion over wide territories, could do much to advance our knowledge, especially if more cooperation could be achieved between the different countries. Now that the methods for such studies are becoming established, and the main outlines of the physiological mechanisms are emerging, the time is ripe for an international attack of this sort.

Education

The problem of educating people in underdeveloped countries is basically the same in animal production as in plant production, but certain special aspects call for comment. Probably the greatest difficulty is in convincing those tied to a "land-to-mouth" existence that the incorporation of animals will, in the end, improve the farm economy. As has been noted, the concept of group or national improvement is too remote in application and in time to evoke a ready response. Under such circumstances the initial educational effort would probably be better directed at men with regional influence than at the individual farmer. Even then it must be attended with considerable patience. It would be wise, in general, to start with improving those animals which are obviously indispensable to the prevailing farm practices, such as the draft animals, and to proceed to food-giving animals by stages, again taking familiar animals such as poultry and swine, or the dairy cow first. With a more complex economy where animals are already part of the farming operations, education may be directed at either of two goals: (a) improvement of practices by the individual farmer, or (b) improvement or institution of herd operations. The relative importance of the two goals will vary with local circumstances. The former will be handicapped by the overwhelming importance of immediate cost and the difficulty for the individual of securing capital. The latter may meet with resistance from the wealthy owner who is well enough off with things the way they are, even though the population as a whole is not. Special difficulties may be encountered where the desirable course of action is the conversion of a backyard to a stockyard plane of operation. Educational efforts must be carefully planned to meet the local conditions and requirements in a realistic fashion. They will be more likely to succeed if they are combined with other types of direct help than if they are presented baldly as educational programs.

Once some appreciation of reformed practices is aroused,

the adviser may find himself embarrassed by having to work as hard restraining enthusiasms as he formerly fought to have reform accepted. Certain aspects of technological practices have acquired a glamor and reputation out of proportion to their usefulness, and especially out of proportion to their applicability to local conditions. A desire for the biggest, brightest, and best is not confined to the American; in fact, social conditions in some less developed countries may actually enhance the prestige value of owning or being associated with the latest in technological show-pieces. Those in charge of educational policy have a considerable responsibility for maintaining a judicious balance and for reiterating the point that problems are seldom solved by the enthusiastic adoption of one or two spectacular methods. Problems are nearly always complex; their solutions can seldom be simple. Practices which work well in one locality may not work at all well in another. Technological devices which suit a technological setting may need considerable modification before they will truly serve a more primitive community.

By far the most serious educational problem is posed by social proscriptions, especially where these have been incorporated into a body of religious or semireligious beliefs. Excessive populations of cattle and monkeys which yield nothing cannot be reduced as long as their elimination is hindered by religious beliefs. Adequate dietary protein is virtually impossible for people who refuse to eat any animal products for fear of religious transgression. A very useful source of both protein and fat is denied to many an ill-nourished family not permitted to eat pork. But any frontal attack upon religious beliefs is likely to provoke considerable resentment and achieve very little good. Those who wish for change—and their number includes many who are themselves subject to those beliefs—must wait patiently for the adjustments that come to all long-standing codes when the interpretations of fundamental verities get sufficiently out of step with individual necessities.

PREFERENTIAL TREATMENT

The problem of deciding where best to invest the money or effort that is available for improving animal production is the same as in crop production. In some respects the decision here may be of even greater moment, since proofs will be longer in coming forward, and mistakes more difficult to rectify. In general, it would seem logical to place the emphasis on those economies in which animals already play a role, and to concentrate there upon improving the desirable features (selection of better types, increased care, betterment of pastures) and discouraging the bad (overstocking, lack of attention). To the extent, however, that virtually insurmountable difficulties result from prohibitions, lack of educational systems, or unreliability of season better results might be obtained where there are potentialities for animal production which have not yet been exploited.

The geographical nature of a country will influence many particular decisions. Beef cattle can be turned out to run on large tracts of relatively poor land, provided that provision is made for the transport of the animals or their carcasses to the centers of consumption. Merino sheep actually do better on poor than on good pasture; but medium-wool sheep require good food. Dairy cattle require intensive handling and their products must be transported daily to the consumers, so that they tend to be associated with urban development. Large-scale swine production calls for supplementary grain feeding, but village production may be adequate for scattered populations. Poultry and goats can be easily maintained in village or rural communities, but large-scale handling is feasible only in advanced centers. Bioclimatic and economic surveys are required to determine these aspects.

There is no golden rule for decisions of this nature. All of the nuances mentioned in connection with crop production —political expediency, economic balance, governmental stability, social attitudes—must be taken into consideration and an individual comprehensive judgment made by someone experienced in these complex affairs.

Chapter 5

HUMAN HEALTH AND EFFICIENCY

THE SUBJECT of this chapter is the effect of tropical climate
on human health and efficiency, with regard to its significance for the economic development of those regions. We
have already seen that the available dietary supply of calories
in tropical countries often falls short of requirements (Table
4), and that such important components as proteins are in
even worse case (Table 6). Further on in this chapter more
evidence will be presented to indicate the prevalence of malnutrition in many tropical countries. From this, one can expect that man's efficiency would be seriously diminished
there; but it would be more instructive to have direct evidence of undue ill-health and poor productivity.

Table 13 classifies the countries of the world according
to income per capita. Such comparisons are not very precise, because of the variation in the purchasing power of
the theoretical dollar from one country to another, the varying requirements of the people, and for other reasons. Nevertheless, the main lines of the picture they show are undoubtedly accurate. The majority of the tropical countries
stand far down on the scale. The economic return to a
worker in tropical countries, and, by implication, the value
of his output are generally very low.

Health is another index of social and economic efficiency.
On its significance, the following quotations are pertinent
(48b):

Health is defined in the preamble to the Constitution of the
World Health Organization as "a state of complete physical,
mental and social well-being and not merely the absence of
disease and infirmity," and the Universal Declaration of Human
Rights declares that "Everyone has the right to a standard of
living adequate for the health and well-being of himself and of
his family, including food, clothing, housing and medical

Table 13

COUNTRIES CLASSIFIED BY SIZE OF PER CAPITA INCOME IN 1950 SHOWING REGIONAL DIVISIONS (48b)

Per capita incomes in U.S. dollars	Africa	Middle East	Asia	Europe (including U.S.S.R.)	Northern America	Latin America	Oceania
1,000 and above	—				United States		Australia New Zealand
600-999	—			Belgium Denmark Norway Sweden Switzerland United Kingdom	Canada		
450-599		Israel		France Luxembourg Netherlands		Argentina Cuba Puerto Rico Uruguay Venezuela	
300-449	—			Czechoslovakia Finland Germany (West) Ireland Poland U.S.S.R.			

Table 13 (cont.)

Per capita incomes in U.S. dollars	Africa	Middle East	Asia	Europe (including U.S.S.R.)	Northern America	Latin America	Oceania
150-299	Union of South Africa	—		Austria Hungary Italy Portugal Yugoslavia	—	Chile Jamaica Panama	—
100-149	Rhodesia (South)	Egypt Lebanon Syria Turkey	Japan Philippines	Greece		Brazil Colombia Costa Rica El Salvador Mexico Nicaragua Peru	
Below 100	Belgian Congo Ethiopia Kenya Liberia Nyasaland Rhodesia (North)	Afghanistan Iran Iraq Saudi Arabia Yemen	Burma Ceylon China India Indonesia Pakistan Thailand			Bolivia Dominican Republic Ecuador Guatemala Haiti Honduras Paraguay	

care . . ." In these terms "health" is not just a medical matter; it is a social goal. It is a goal difficult to achieve because, while the community, if it makes the effort, can provide the means and services—public health measures, sanitation, better treatment of disease and fuller amenities—health, in the final analysis, depends also on the individual. . . .

. . . . .

The saying that the health of a people is the wealth of a people is not merely a pious aphorism. Certainly the converse is true, that a community burdened with ill-health is an impoverished community. There is a vicious circle; disease—under-production—poverty—poor health services—more disease, which is manifested in those underdeveloped countries where the majority of a people are afflicted with gross diseases which rob them of vitality and initiative and which create social lethargy. A peasant, sick of a fever at the critical periods of planting and harvesting, cannot grow enough food, or earn enough to buy it. Malnutrition, in turn, exposes him to infectious and other diseases. Not only are he and his family impoverished but all the standards of his community are degraded physically and in morale.

One of the best indices of the economic effect of ill-health is life expectancy, since it indicates in a fairly direct fashion the opportunity that each individual has to repay the community for the cost of his birth and upbringing. The additional economic loss resulting from incapacity short of death may be taken as running fairly parallel with that induced by death. Some statistics on expectation of life at birth in tropical, as compared with temperate countries, are given in Table 14.

From Table 14 it will be seen that the expectation of life is certainly low in some tropical countries. But it will be equally clear that the differences do not follow a strict climatic sequence, suggesting instead the influence of other factors which might be ascribed to that general background of custom called culture.

Infant deaths represent an economic loss as well as failure of medical care. Infant mortality rates, i.e. deaths under

Table 14

LIFE EXPECTANCY AT BIRTH AND INFANT MORTALITY

Country	Year	Expectancy (male)	Year	Infant mortality per 1,000 live births
Belgian Congo	1950-52	37.6		
Egypt	1936-38	35.6	1951	128.6
Gold Coast			1951	118.0
Madagascar			1952	90.7
Nigeria			1953	81.7
Northern Rhodesia			1953	29.0
Uganda			1950	87.6
Union of South Africa	1945-47			
white		63.8	1954	34.2
Asian		50.7		
Burma			1953	230.5
Ceylon	1952	57.7	1954	72.0
India	1941-50	32.5	1953	119.1
Israel	1954	67.5		
Japan	1953	61.9	1953	48.9
Pakistan			1951	110.3
Philippines			1952	108.7
Thailand	1947-48	48.7	1953	64.9
Costa Rica	1949-51	55.7[1]	1954	101.2
Dominican Republic			1954	68.3
Jamaica	1950-52	55.7	1954	66.1
Mexico	1940	37.9	1954	80.5
Panama	1941-43	50.5	1954	50.4
Argentina	1947	56.9	1954	61.9
Chile	1952	49.8	1954	123.8
Colombia			1954	102.7
British Guiana	1945-47	49.3	1954	73.9
Ecuador	1949-51	50.4	1949	115.2
Venezuela			1954	68.0

Table 14 (cont.)

Country	Year	Expectancy (male)	Year	Infant mortality per 1,000 live births
Italy	1935-37	57.5[2]	1954	52.8
Portugal	1949-52	55.5	1954	85.5
United Kingdom	1953	67.3	1954	26.3
United States	1952		1954	
white		66.6		26.6
other		59.1		
Australia	1946-48	66.1	1954	22.5

[1] Expectancy at birth of male and female combined.
[2] Expectancy at birth of female population.
Source: United Nations, *Demographic Yearbook, 1955*, (New York, 1955).

twelve months of age per 1,000 live births, are also given in Table 14 for the same or similar countries. Being high in some tropical countries, they show much the same trend as life-expectancy data but again are apparently related as much to culture as to climate.

From the evidence it would seem, therefore, that human welfare and productivity are at a low ebb in many tropical countries, but that the level is not strictly related to climate. It becomes necessary, therefore, to review the evidence that may permit us to separate the climatic from the nonclimatic effects before assessing the significance of the former upon human economy.

THE EFFECTS OF CLIMATE

Before the turn of the century the multifarious disabilities that were wont to oppress the tropical dweller were usually ascribed to the vague but all-inclusive influence of "climate." This tendency, indeed, is memorialized in the very name *malaria*, or bad air. As the germ theory of disease became accepted, as the complicated life-histories of many infective agents were elucidated, and as the scientific basis of tropical medicine was laid, the concept changed. For many, the effect of tropical climate came to be almost entirely an indirect one, operating through its influence on infectious agents and their vectors. Of recent years, however, the increasing control of infectious disease has revealed other modes of climatic operation. Indirect effects through malnutrition, as well as direct effects upon the individual person, have acquired a greater relative importance, although there is still much confusion in the public mind. Traces of the nineteenth-century attitude—that tropical disabilities are the inevitable toll of the climate—can still be found. The importance of man's activities, or culture, in favoring or counteracting the deleterious effects of climate are often overlooked. The great difficulty experienced by the temperate dweller upon entering the tropics of adapting his old ways to the new environment gets too little recognition. Before we can make a valid assessment of the influence of climate as such upon economic development in the tropics, and especially before we can plan countermeasures effectively, we need to recognize the various ways in which climate affects human welfare and the influence of certain nonclimatic factors therein. A considerable amount of effort has been expended in trying to disentangle the various interactions. While very much more work needs to be done, useful information has already been obtained as will be seen from what follows.

Direct Physiological Effects

As in most fields of scientific inquiry, the earlier attempts to study the direct effects of climate upon man usually followed the statistical survey method; that is, the investigator looked for correlations between easily recognizable disturbances and easily recorded climatic events. For collecting ideas that may repay further study this method is both useful and valid; but it has certain very severe limitations. In the first place, it cannot *prove* anything; all that it does is to show certain associations, without saying anything about essential relationships of cause and effect. A certain disturbance may be associated statistically with a certain climatic pattern, but so also may a lot of other things not indicated by the statistical data. The disturbance might well be due to one or more of those other things, rather than to the climate itself—indeed, this is precisely what has transpired in very many instances. In the second place, in applying statistical methods only to those things for which statistical data are available, one is likely to miss entirely other factors which may be most important links in the chain of cause and effect. Third, the unreliability of raw statistical data, common enough in technological countries, may completely becloud the issue for many of the areas in which we are interested.

Suggestions thrown up by the statistical survey method call for further study, preferably by the experimental method. Unfortunately, restraint did not always characterize the writings of those who used evidence collected in this way. Too often, where ideas suggested by the preliminary evidence were in accord with attitudes and policies already adopted by the temperate sojourners in the tropics, they were eagerly seized upon as scientific justification. In this fashion a folklore was established which was not seriously disturbed until success in military operations in World War II cast doubt upon its validity.

The experimental method, however, cannot stand alone. It feeds upon the ideas generated by survey methods and must have its conclusions verified in turn by practical test. In essence, it relies upon two procedures: (a) studying the action of influences one at a time, while holding all the others constant; and (b) setting up a test situation to see if things happen in the way that theory suggests they should happen. It is difficult, however, to devise adequate experimental studies of many situations, and the answers obtained are apt to be no more than partial or special solutions. They are always attended, moreover, by a certain degree of artificiality. However true the answer may be for the particular conditions of the experiment, the circumstances under which the problem arises in nature are apt to be different, so that the answer may need modification or interpretation before it can be applied to actual conditions. Nevertheless, experimental operations are repeatable and verifiable by anyone who chooses to question the results. In the study of climatic effects upon man, the usual three phases can be seen: (1) recognition of the problem, often with the aid of the statistical survey method; (2) analytical studies, usually in the laboratory; and (3) synoptic studies, in which attempts are made to see the problem and its answers whole, often in the field.

Analytical studies to date have dealt mainly with the effect of single variables (temperature, humidity, etc.), or with simple combinations of variables two or three at a time. A respectable body of knowledge of this kind has been built up (32); but it has not been easy to discover a general theory by means of which the combined effect of several variables can be ascertained or a prediction made concerning the probable effect of conditions not specifically studied. Figure 5 shows a tentative chart devised by the author for predicting the significance of given conditions of temperature and humidity upon a person carrying out moderate activity while dressed in summer clothing. The oblique line running through the point corresponding to any given temperature and humidity indicates the *thermal strain* developed in a moderately acclimatized person. The significance of this strain can be gauged from the accompanying tabulation. The formula upon which this chart is based enables similar calculations to be made for other degrees of activity, types of clothing, and rates of air movement. The effect of radiation can also be incorporated. If further checking proves this formulation reliable, it will represent a distinct step forward in the approach to the practical application of existing knowledge.

The application of knowledge to practical field problems is beset with many difficulties. For example, if climagrams are superimposed upon a climatic strain chart (Figure 6), a fair comparative idea may be expected of the net climatic strain. But it must be remembered that the strain chart is based upon the reactions of only partially experienced people to short exposures to heat. Application to people continuously living in hot climates is made uncertain by the inadequacy of present knowledge on long-term effects. Continued exposure involves elements of both improved adaptation and cumulative deterioration, the nature and relative significance of which have been insufficiently studied. Again, natural climates embrace many more factors than those involved in the simpler question of heat balance, the importance of which cannot very well be written into equations. In the face of such uncertainties, decisions must necessarily involve a large measure of personal judgment; and personal judgment, such as that used by the physician in diagnosis, must be based upon a wide, continuing, and critical experience if it is to be at all reliable. Unfortunately, few of those called upon to exercise judgment have such a range of experience. Scientists are apt to be specialists; administrators are apt to be geographically confined.

The evidence so far accumulated along these lines may be summed up as follows:

a) People who are unaccustomed to the climatic conditions of the tropics experience many direct physiological effects which impair their efficiency, sometimes to the point of clinical disturbance.

b) With continued experience, the major disturbances tend to disappear in about ten days, although longer periods are required for complete acclimatization.

Note on Figure 5

To use: find the point corresponding to the particular temperature and humidity under consideration; the position of this point in relation to the numbered oblique lines indicates the relative strain to be expected in a man doing light work and normally clad, when the rate of air movement is moderate.

The significance of the degree of strain can be gauged from the following list:

No persons comfortable below	2–4
Most persons comfortable	3½–6
None comfortable above	7½–12
Commencing deterioration in muscular performance	12
Recommended upper limit for daily work	14–18
Commencing deterioration in mental performance	30
Distress in 2 hours, failure in 5 hours	40
Distress in 1 hour	60
Loss of alertness, failure in 2 hours	100

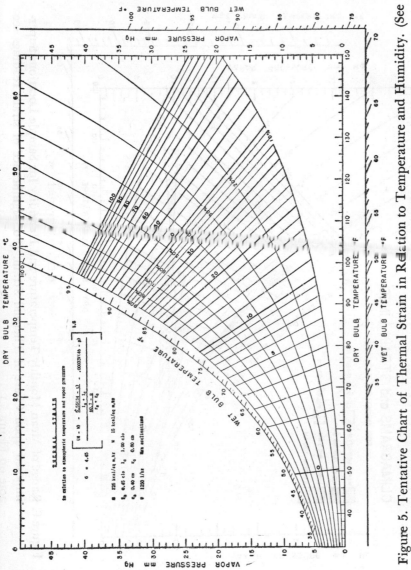

Figure 5. Tentative Chart of Thermal Strain in Relation to Temperature and Humidity. (See note on opposite page.)

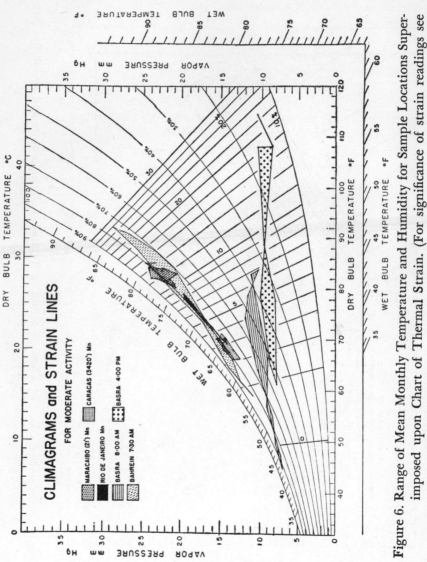

Figure 6. Range of Mean Monthly Temperature and Humidity for Sample Locations Superimposed upon Chart of Thermal Strain. (For significance of strain readings see note on Figure 5.)

c) While the capacity of men for physical work is little changed when acclimatization is complete, there remains an increased disinclination for work which tends to reduce normal output.

d) Appropriate incentives can restore output to levels characteristic of temperate regions, at least temporarily.

e) Apart from a reduced desire for activity, there seem to be no permanent deleterious *direct* climatic effects in healthy persons living under natural conditions in the tropics.

f) Artificial conditions, such as those in hot industries or badly designed houses, may continue to produce physiological disturbances in acclimatized persons.

Direct Psychological Effects

With the physiological effects of climate at a minimum, and pathological effects (see page 119) coming under control, the psychological effects assume an ever-increasing importance. There is no gainsaying the importance of the psychological effects of tropical climates. Most newcomers from temperate climes experience a disinclination to work, mentally as well as physically. This, as was suggested above, may have a physiological basis and may subside to a certain extent with adaptation. But there are those who question whether the customary level of activity and initiative is ever restored, or whether those born and raised in tropical climates ever aspire to the degree of activity characteristic of cooler environments.

Certainly, the usual pattern of life in tropical countries is more leisurely and less productive of material goods than that which is found in most temperate latitudes, and a case can be made for at least some influence of climate in this respect. Man in the temperate zones has built up his civilizations around the important demands created by cold weather for securing food and shelter in advance. In so doing, he has developed a culture in which activity and making provision for the future have high social values. These social reflexes may be reinforced by conditioned physiological reflexes in men who are accustomed to such conditions. In tropical populations, on the other hand, climate provides neither the social nor the physiological drive for activity and saving beyond the needs of the more or less immediate future. This difference in "spontaneous" activity marks one of the most important conflicts at the personal level between temperate and tropical modes of behavior.

There is a general tendency to answer questions about possible levels of activity in the tropics in a gloomy fashion and to cite past performances in support. But what has been, is not necessarily what has to be—a Roman soldier stationed in Britain would no doubt have been skeptical about the future productivity of the barbarous inhabitants in so vile a climate; and many a colonial governor has recorded grave disapproval of areas which are now highly successful. Conversely, there have been flourishing empires in areas that are truly tropical (e.g., Southeast Asia) and intense activity can be found today in more than one tropical area (e.g., Venezuela).

The problem of possible levels of activity has not been adequately studied, at least with the objectivity that science requires. Such studies as have been made demonstrate quite clearly that the nature of the individual profoundly affects his reaction. Unmotivated persons may show a marked drop in efficiency of performance under conditions which appear not to affect the well-motivated individual (26). In the total environment of tropical countries numerous and powerful nonclimatic factors are ever present to disturb and modify the pattern of behavior characteristic of temperate-zone countries. These need to be identified and counteracted if comparable levels of productivity and efficiency are to be pursued.

Specific psychological disturbances arising in the course of exposure to hot conditions may be summarized as follows:

a) Some loss of mental initiative is probably the most important single direct result of exposure to tropical environment.

b) Accuracy may be noticeably affected in poorly motivated persons, but relatively undisturbed in well-adapted ones, except under rather extreme or unusual conditions.

c) A person may feel that the performance of a given task calls for more concentration under hot conditions, without showing any deterioration in actual performance.

Table 15

INCIDENCE OF TROPICAL DISEASES

Country	Population (48c, 1952)	Malaria (new cases)	Filariasis	Hookworm	Schistosoma hematobium	Schistosoma mansoni	Yaws (new cases)
1. Guatemala	2,787,030	39,393 ('50)	under 10%	over 20%	—	—	x
2. Honduras	1,368,605	12,003 ('52)	—	over 20%	—	—	No deaths
3. Br. Honduras	59,220	1,003 ('47)	—	10-20%	—	—	x
4. El Salvador	1,855,917	11,009	under 10%	over 20%	—	—	x
5. Nicaragua	1,053,189	2,883 ('52)	—	over 20%	—	—	4 cases ('52)
6. Costa Rica	800,875	8,797 ('52)	under 10%	over 20%	—	—	112 cases ('52)
7. Panama	805,285	1,886 ('52)	under 10%	over 20%	—	—	4 cases ('46)
8. Cuba	4,778,583	162 ('52)	under 10%	10-20%	—	—	12,205 cases ('47)
9. Jamaica	1,237,063	medium	under 10%	under 20%	—	—	3,056 cases ('52)
10. Haiti	3,111,973	13,815 ('52)	under 10%	over 20%	—	—	4,686 cases ('52)
11. Dom. Republic	2,121,683	15,450 ('52)	under 10%	over 20%	—	—	—
12. Puerto Rico	2,210,703	94 ('52)	6 cases ('47)	over 20%	—	10%	x
13. Virgin Islands	26,665	x	under 10%	over 20%	—	under 10%	958 cases ('47)
14. Trinidad	557,970	2,282 ('50)	under 10%	7,767 ('47)	—	under 10%	x
15. Fr. W. Indies	567,000	x	under 10%	over 20%	—	under 10%	x
16. Dutch W. Indies	163,000	x	under 10%	over 20%	—	under 10%	x
17. Br. W. Indies	2,088,495	x	under 10%	over 20%	—	under 10%	—
18. Br. Guiana	414,887	5,269 ('47)	10-20%	over 20%	—	under 10%	37 cases ('47)
19. Surinam	216,000	8 deaths	10-20%	over 20%	—	under 10%	x
20. Fr. Guiana	28,506	x	10-20%	over 20%	—	under 10%	light infection
21. Venezuela	4,985,716	8,667 ('52)	10-20%	over 20%	—	over 20%	1,955 ('52)
22. Colombia	11,266,075	73,993 ('52)	under 10%	65,817 ('52)	—	—	3,083
23. Ecuador	3,202,757	2,259 ('52)	—	over 20% on coast	—	—	18 ('52)
24. Peru	6,207,967	17,733 ('52)	—	10-20%	—	under 10%	475 ('52)
25. Fr. W. Africa	6,524,000	20-80%	10-90%	10-90%	10-20%	under 10%	heavy infection

Table 15 (cont.)

Country	Population (48c, 1952)	Malaria (new cases)	Filariasis	Hookworm	Schistosoma hematobium	Schistosoma mansoni	Yaws (new cases)
26. Fr. Eq. Af.	4,406,000	55%	10-over 20%	30-100%	25-80%	under 10%	7.3-14.75% medium infection
27. Nigeria	22,987,550	100,000+	27%	15-30%	31.6%	15.2%	30,000 ('50)
28. Gold Coast	3,735,682	60,000	21%	40-50%	10-20%	under 10%	144,400 ('50)
29. Ivory Coast	4,056,000	20-80%	10-over 20%	30-90%	11%	under 10%	63%
30. Liberia	1,500,000	21-34%	14-20%	59-80%	under 10%	under 10%	107,300 ('48)
31. Sierra Leone	2,000,000	10,000-30,000	10-20%	over 20%	under 10%	under 10%	7,400 ('49)
32. Port. Guinea	510,777	20-100%	49%	90-95%	10-20%	under 10%	heavy infection
33. Belgian Congo	14,090,877	293,579 ('52)	4,521 ('52)	161,465 ('52)	16,919	2,625 ('52)	217,639 ('52)
34. Angola	4,111,796	50,000-70,000	under 10%	2,800-5,000	4,223 ('52)	—	7,400 ('50)
35. N. Rhodesia	1,837,000	10-15%	under 10%	16-78%	0-61%	—	100 ('50)
36. Tanganyika	7,477,677	132,700 ('47)	25-90%	25-40%	33-94%	17%	61,800 ('49)
37. Uganda	4,958,520	40,000-120,000	10-over 20%	over 20%	50%	30%	24,500 ('50)
38. Kenya	5,186,966	57,000-110,000	up to 40%	10-over 20%	over 20%	10-20%	10,500 ('50)
39. Somalia	1,021,572	50-90%	under 10%	55-75%	under 10%	—	250-650 cases ('47)
40. Ethiopia	7,500,000	20-20%	—	—	under 10%	under 10%	medium infection
41. Sudan	7,931,150	200,000-350,000	15-20%	—	8.7%	1.1%	31,700 ('50)
42. Br. Somaliland	500,000	2791 at least	under 10%	—	—	—	x
43. Fr. Somaliland	56,000	1,429-2,475	—	6%	under 10%	under 10%	x
44. Yemen	4,500,000	heavy infection	10-20%	—	under 10%	under 10%	400 ('49)
45. S. Rhodesia	2,158,330	heavy infection	—	0-23%	10-30%	3-16%	x
46. Ceylon	6,657,339	2,933,074 ('42)	10-20%	90-99%	—	—	3,000
47. Indochina	27,030,000	about 1/5 pop.	10-20%	50%	—	—	97,442
48. Thailand	17,442,689	50,000	10-20%	52.8%	—	—	25,000
49. Malaya	4,908,086	40%	10-36%	27-90%	—	—	over 11,000
50. Singapore	1,041,933	x	—	over 20%	—	—	x

Table 15 (cont.)

Country	Population (48c, 1952)	Malaria (new cases)	Filariasis	Hookworm	Schistosoma hematobium	Schistosoma mansoni	Yaws (new cases)
51. Indonesia	60,412,962	10-90%	10-50%	over 20%	—	—	10-90%
52. N. Borneo	348,000	2-70%	10-20%	10-over 20%	—	—	medium infection
53. Sarawak	562,000	2-70%	10-20%	10-over 20%	—	—	medium infection
54. New Guinea	333,631	26-43%	10-20%	10-over 20%	—	—	6-7%
55. New Britain	93,837	23-52%	—	—	—	—	x
56. Timor	439,000	heavy infection	10-20%	over 20%	—	—	80-90%
57. Philippines	19,234,182	1,000,000-2,000,000	under 10%	10-20%	—	up to 80%	31,647 at least
58. New Caledonia	61,250	—	20-25%	over 20%	—	—	599 ('47)
59. Fiji	259,638	4 cases ('50)	30.4%	0.5-60%	—	—	medium infection
60. Hawaii	499,794	x	under 10%	21 cases ('42)	—	—	—
61. Carolinas	48,048	—	under 10%	40-50%	—	—	light infection
62. Solomons	94,066	25-63%	at least 0.6%	over 20%	—	—	40,000
63. Marianas	44,025	—	6 cases	40-50%	—	—	light infection
64. Marshalls	10,446	—	10-20%	40-50%	—	—	light infection
65. Hong Kong	840,473	608 ('47)	under 10%	over 20%	light J infection	?	no deaths
66. Macao	374,737	x	—	?	—	—	—

x = disease occurs but statistics not available.   — = disease does not occur.
? = no information on this disease.   J = Japonicum.
Source: Data provided by Jacques May (see 28).

d) While tropical conditions may provide the opportunity or excuse for personality changes, there is no reason to believe that these conditions are any more potent in provoking such changes than numerous other life situations.

Climate, on the other hand, is a convenient bogeyman to be blamed for psychological difficulties whose real origin is much more personal.

Disease

The relationship between tropical climates and human infectious disease is very similar to that already discussed in connection with animals, and even plants. In the precarious ecological situation of the tropics a balance can be maintained only by the interaction of many forces, each of which is being continuously adjusted to the effects of the others. The ease with which infectious disease develops is due only in part to the favorable medium provided for both organism and vector by the equable climate. It is also due to the probability that from among the multiplicity of micro-organisms there is almost bound to be one which will exploit any new niche that is presented, especially if the niche is provided by a species that is imposing an imbalance upon the precarious resources. Into this unstable complex, man must enter as a competitor. If he is to survive, he must fit in. This he can do only as long as his demands are limited and self-replacing.

Table 15, furnished by Jacques May, indicates the enormous incidence, even today, of tropical infectious disease. To the specifically "tropical" diseases must be added the more or less universal infectious diseases like tuberculosis, which are far from discouraged by the social and climatic conditions found in the tropics. On the etiological complex, May expressed himself in a paper prepared for the Study Group as follows:

Whether man is affected by climate to such a degree that he partly loses his biological stamina and some of his ability to control the environment, or whether the kinds, numbers, and varieties of external aggressors upon his organism are greater in the tropics than in temperate climates, is a problem of such complicated magnitude that it can probably not be solved at this point. When we find tropical man living with three million red cells per cubic millimeter [normal, five and a half million], supporting ascarids and hookworms, and having at one time or another suffered from malarial infection to the point where the scars still exist in his reticuloendothelial system, it is quite impossible to state which of those causes is dominant, which influent, and how they combine to produce among others this physiological feature of low red cell count. No comparison with the white man living in the tropics is valid, for the white man brings with him a control over the environment which makes him less vulnerable to outside attacks than the native. There are some indications that, if placed in exactly similar conditions, he will acquire the same disease-fostering parasites, with the same harmful effects upon his physiology. No experimentation artificially induced has so far reproduced all the causes found in nature which can be blamed for impaired physiology, so that the problem is without a solution. Yet it can be assumed that the low oxygen-carrying capacity of tropical populations as a whole is important in governing their physical and mental development. Their tissues are submitted to a permanent semi-anoxia. Their culture has provided them with ways whereby they can survive as a group, but it has not developed in the direction where the individual's survival should be long and pleasant, which is characteristic of our type of culture. As long as the species reproduces itself in increasing numbers the mysterious requirements of natural laws seem to be satisfied, there being no provision in these laws for pleasantness and duration of individual life. . . . Those diseases which affect large numbers . . . have different ways of lowering man's aggressiveness towards his environment. Blood tissue and organ infections such as malaria, filariasis, schistosomiasis, permanent fungal infections, and many others act upon human physiology in different ways. Most of these various parasites affect blood, tissues, and organs at various stages of their life cycle.

Tropical man can thus be viewed as constantly subjected to the spoliating or toxic action of millions of larval or adult forms of exogenous life. At the same time he is starving. The point before us is to decide whether these factors are the dominant ones in creating the type of ecological adaptation which is common in the tropical world, and which results in the state of affairs we want to modify for our benefit and theirs.

Whatever the relative importance of the various factors involved, it is abundantly clear from the data presented that infectious disease is prevalent indeed in the tropical regions. It is clear, furthermore, that this widespread incidence of debilitating, incapacitating, and life-shortening disease must seriously reduce both the desire for work and the efficiency of performance, and that these effects will in turn increase the likelihood of malnutrition and decrease the efficacy of preventive measures in a self-perpetuating cycle of poverty and disease. In Fred L. Soper's words, "the first measure of the economic burden of disease to a given country is the mean life expectancy of the population." For peoples living under different economic and social conditions measures of life expectancy are more sensitive and compared more easily than figures based on money values.

Malnutrition

From the data given in previous chapters in connection with crop and animal production, it is abundantly evident that few tropical countries produce enough food to provide an adequate supply of calories, protein, or supplementary nutrients for more than a small and favored fraction of their populations. It is clear from the very term "underdeveloped" that these countries are, with few exceptions, unlikely to produce enough other commodities to make good by exchange the deficiencies in food production. It would be safe to conclude from these figures alone that an important part of the tropical peoples is underfed. These conclusions are further supported by surveys made of the available statistics for tropical countries by the American Geographical Society, with the following results:

Three countries have adequate diets: Portuguese Guinea, Somalia, Thailand.

Twenty-four countries have diets providing adequate energy value but inadequate protective elements: Guatemala, Cuba, Dominican Republic, Trinidad, British Guiana, Surinam, French West Africa, French Equatorial Africa, Nigeria, Gold

Coast, Belgian Congo, Uganda, Sudan, Indo-China, North Borneo, Sarawak, New Guinea, New Caledonia, Fiji, Caroline Islands, Solomon Islands, Mariana Islands, Marshall Islands, Bechuanaland.

Forty-seven countries are inadequate on both counts: Honduras, British Honduras, El Salvador, Nicaragua, Costa Rica, Panama, Jamaica, Haiti, Puerto Rico, Virgin Islands, French West Indies, Dutch West Indies, British West Indies, French Guiana, Venezuela, Colombia, Ecuador, Peru, Ivory Coast, Liberia, Sierra Leone, Angola, Northern Rhodesia, Tanganyika, Kenya, Ethiopia, British Somaliland, French Somaliland, Southern Rhodesia, Ceylon, Malaya, Singapore, Indonesia, Timor, Philippines, Hong Kong, Macao, Mexico, Bolivia, Brazil, Oman, Mozambique, Madagascar, Mauritius, South-West Africa, Burma, India, (J. May)

The extent to which this state of affairs may be attributed to the climate has been indicated in previous chapters. The high rainfall and prevailing warm temperatures promote the loss of nitrogenous and mineral nutrients from the soil-plant cycle, reduce the yield and nutritive value of crops, impair the growth and yield of animals dependent upon the soil and its crops, and interfere with the work of harvesting, transportation, and storage. On the other hand, numerous social and economic factors join hands with climate to reduce still further the availability and utilization of food material. Certainly the chronically underfed person is in a poor position to meet either the direct climatic stresses or the indirect effects through disease. It would indeed be surprising if he adopted aggressive and progressive attitudes toward his environment and his future. In May's words:

As a result of these various starvation patterns not only is the will to survive lessened but incapacitating deficiency diseases are fostered upon large sections of the population. The study made at the American Geographical Society shows all the tropical belt ridden with various groups of vitamin deficiency diseases as well as protein deficiency syndromes, the most recently described of which, *kwashiorkor*, is of particular interest. First it seems to be common over large areas outside Africa where it has first been described. Second, the map of kwashiorkor seems to coincide with the map of fatty degeneration of the liver in early adult-hood and perhaps also, although this needs further confirmation, with the map of primary carcinoma of the liver. Thus we find that the populations of the lands under consideration do not enjoy the health and the well-being upon which our modern Western culture is based, because they starve for a number of reasons: soil, technology, taboos, overcrowding, poverty, financial-social structure. The problem in this respect would seem to be to find a way whereby these people could be fed. Listing the causes for this starvation underscores the difficulty of solving that problem.

CIRCUMVENTING THE EFFECTS

Certainly much can be done, and much has already been done, to limit the effects of tropical climates upon man himself; but this is a struggle in which there can be no respite, no standing still. The tropical environment is always present to exert its full influence if our guard is relaxed; it is always ready to spring some new development, some unexpected threat, when all seems secure. As knowledge advances and as successful methods are developed for establishing man's mastery in a particular sector, the pattern changes. This calls for change in plans of attack, a flexibility of thought and action which can benefit more from the principles than from the details of past successes. Some of the sectors more open to attack may be briefly reviewed.

Public Health

In its widest sense, the term *public health* can be used to include all measures directed at improving the health of the community, but it will be used here to signify those measures for the reduction of disease which involve community rather than individual action. Public health in the tropics must first attempt to do what it does in temperate zones, namely, institute programs of sanitation which aim at preventing the occurrence and transmission of disease in general. Beyond this, it must consider combatting the special ways in which tropical conditions tend to promote disease and institute such special measures as may be necessary to break the life-cycle of specifically tropical diseases. This is a colossal task, made no easier by the difficulty of getting technical personnel or by the lack of understanding shown by the population. It can be done, but at a cost, and only with patience.

Many of the necessary measures have already achieved historical distinction. Who does not know the story of the conquest of yellow fever in the building of the Panama Canal, or the control of malaria in the fighting forces of World War II? Of equal importance are the battles being fought each day, without much attention and sometimes with only limited success, but constantly extending man's dominion over infectious agents in tropical and subtropical areas.

Continuous attention to rat control has practically abolished plague from some countries and is markedly restricting it in others. Insecticides have worked wonders in reducing the incidence of mosquito-borne diseases in many places although jubilation must be tempered by the realization that in some areas strains of mosquito have developed which are resistant to the controlling compound. Inoculation with vaccines has very markedly reduced the incidence of cholera in India's swarming pilgrimages. Injections of penicillin have largely banished yaws from Haiti. Antimalarial suppressants have now reached the point where the taking of one or two completely unobjectionable tablets a week will prevent the onset of all but the most intense infections. Stringent measures for controlling the mosquito responsible for carrying urban yellow fever have practically eliminated the mosquito from all of the Americas (except certain portions of the United States and Argentina). A similar campaign has been successfully waged against the malaria mosquito in Egypt.

A rise in the standards of living may often be attended by a decline in the incidence or severity of certain infectious diseases. The disappearance of malaria from England and many parts of Italy, and of yellow fever from the United States, seems to have taken place to an extent and at a rate out of proportion to specific control measures. It is apparently associated with a generally improved state of nutrition and general health. General sanitary and nutritional measures are undoubtedly important, but for reliable and quick results specific measures will usually be necessary as well, provided that they are correctly applied. However, specific measures taken alone will meet with less than expected success if low levels of general hygiene are allowed to persist.

The cost of public health programs is usually not very great, and in some cases surprisingly low. As reported by Fred L. Soper, the Rockefeller Foundation spent about $14 million on yellow fever control over a period of 35 years, but so successfully that the countries concerned have now taken over most of the maintenance costs. The cost of each penicillin injection used in Haiti for the control of yaws is only 4½ cents. The return to the community in longer and more efficient life greatly exceeds the initial cost of the campaigns.

Lest optimism run too high, however, the following warning note sounded by Jacques May should be heard:

I would agree that it is theoretically possible: (a) with the proper drugs to cleanse a large proportion of this sick people, (b) with adequate effort and money to create the personnel needed to follow-up the original cleansing in further generations. Yet if all these tropical diseases could be eradicated, I still believe very serious problems would arise. I doubt very much whether such an upset of the present disease and starvation set-up would mean health. I believe that in the world of disease-producing agents the same well-co-ordinated web of life exists that obtains everywhere in nature; that the eradication of the "dominants" and the "influents" would mean the outcrop of other forms, species, and groups; and that instead of eradicating disease we might just bring about a change in the map of disease. Would this improve man's fate? Nobody knows. Yet I would agree that a well-planned, limited effort, local in scope, made on carefully selected places, might succeed for as long as outside help in men and money would be available. I even agree that, in view of the present international situation, it might be advisable to try. Yet I do not think that any spectacular self-perpetuating changes would result. On the contrary, I believe that as soon as the external stimulus would stop, future generations would witness what we always witness in nature when a temporary change has been forced on the ecological picture. The wound thus inflicted in the flesh of nature would quickly heal itself, and the original order of things would be restored.

Housing and Clothing

Dissimilar though they may appear, housing and clothing have many basic purposes in common insofar as both should serve to protect the individual from the addition of external heat, while permitting him to lose the heat he himself produces. There is more than a grain of truth in the humorous statements that Bedouin clothing is simply a tent with a hole for the head, and that if modern temperate housing becomes any smaller and tighter it will simply be a suit of clothes. In a warm humid climate the function of both clothing and housing is to exclude solar radiation and other harmful elements of the environment (insects, jungle, and predators) while offering as little interference as possible to the evaporation of sweat. In the simplest form this means the provision of overhead shade, some form of screening, and the maintenance of air movement over the skin of the occupant.

From the experience of World War II and the scientific investigations which arose out of the experience, the requirements have become fairly well documented; but some difficulty arises when one attempts to meet all the different requirements in one clothing design. Elsewhere I have summarized the position as follows (24b):

The thermal requirement for clothing (in warm humid environments) may be summed up in the phrase—there are no clothes like no clothes! Only by the maximum exposure of skin can ventilation be brought anywhere near optimum rates. In the absence of any strong radiation load, from which protection might be desirable, the net effect of clothing can only be to reduce the opportunities for heat loss. Unfortunately, some clothing is demanded, not only by the dictates of society (and there are very few cultures which do not impose some such requirement), but also as protection against nonthermal hazards of the environment. The annoyance caused by the onslaught of multifarious biting and stinging arthropoda may be neglected with training; but immunity against diseases carried by these vectors is not so easily or cheaply acquired, and at best amounts to little more than a precarious truce. Methods of both vector and disease control have vastly improved of recent years, but they are far from being so reliable that the protective role of clothing may be ignored. There is a strong case for yielding some part of the thermally desirable features, if necessary, to the interests of disease prevention in these humid environments. This, however, must not be taken as justifying complete sacrifice of thermal principles. The rigid enforcement of protection against mosquitoes during World War II in the Pacific undoubtedly contributed to the widespread incidence of so-called "tropical dermatosis." [33] A little less enthusiastic pursuit of the ideal in malarial protection might have established a clinically better compromise. Comfort, moreover, is in itself a desirable objective if situations have to be long endured; and this is certainly difficult to achieve in these environments if extensive clothing is the rule.

The first principle in the design of clothing for warm humid and wet environments is undoubtedly maximum ventilation of the space between clothing and skin, in order to facilitate evaporation. This is most easily obtained by a combination of minimum coverage, looseness of fit, absence of constrictions, and strategic placement of openings to promote through ventilation. In parts subjected to frequent bellows movement, small apertures in the clothing, such as those provided by mesh or net construction, may contribute importantly to this exchange. The second principle is maximum permeability to water vapor of the clothing over those parts inadequately ventilated, so that the accumulating vapor may pass without too much resistance to the exterior. The provision of a screen against direct solar radiation is necessary when that radiation is intense, but it is not required nearly so regularly as it is in hot dry environments. Light colors are similarly desirable where direct solar radiation is likely to be intense, but not necessary under many of the prevailing circumstances.

In housing, as in clothing, poor design can aggravate the natural climatic discomforts, and it would seem only reasonable to avoid such effects wherever possible. Here again the principles can be fairly clearly stated, but the difficulty comes in satisfying the various requirements in the one design and, especially, at low cost. The principles are set forth in Table 16.

Table 16

PRINCIPLES OF HOUSE DESIGN FOR WARM HUMID ENVIRONMENTS (24c)

A. PRINCIPLES

Reducing human heat production	*Reducing gain and promoting losses from body by radiation*	*Promoting losses from body by evaporation*	*Reducing heat liberation in building*
Convenience of arrangement	External shade	Ventilation (volume flow)	Minimize heat and vapor liberation
Ease of cleaning	Reduced ground reflection	Air movement (velocity of flow)	Remove liberated heat and vapor
	Attached shade	Dehumidification	
	Minimal solar projection		
	High reflectivity of exterior		
	Convection over surfaces exposed to radiation		
	Insulation (capacity type) to roof		
	Convection over inner surfaces		
	Low emissivity of inner surfaces		
	Moderate ceiling height		

B. APPLICATIONS

Convenient storage space	Shade trees, especially to roof	Maximum wall openings for breeze, with blinds, louvers, etc. against rain	Capacity insulation around oven and firebox
Convenient plan and conservation of floor space	Shade bushes, etc., especially to east and west exposures, but without obstructing wind	Cross-ventilation directed and without obstruction	Narrow air space lined with aluminum foil in oven wall
Convenient facilities	Separation of buildings	Ventilation of roof space and spaces between successive roofing layers	Liquid or gas fuel, or power, where economically feasible
Easily cleaned surfaces, especially floor	Vegetation over ground	Turbulence-producing fans	Vent to outside over stove

Table 16 (cont.)

Reducing human heat production	Reducing gain and promoting losses from body by radiation	Promoting losses from body by evaporation	Reducing heat liberation in building
	Eaves and other horizontal projections on equatorial exposures	Dehumidification by refrigeration or absorption	Vents and infrared screens for lamps
	Awnings, verandahs, etc., especially on equatorial exposures		Kitchen separate from house
	Vertical projections beside window openings on equatorial exposure		
	Minimum solar projection of roof		
	Light color or polished metal for surfaces exposed to solar radiation		
	Avoid parapets and mutual interference of roof structures to wind		
	Wood, stone, or other material of low diffusivity for roof		
	Ceiling height generally not over eight feet		

Marked advances have been made in the technical aspects of air-conditioning over the last ten years. The present position is indicated in the following summary of remarks presented to the Study Group by E. P. Palmatier:

In a house which is neither heated nor cooled, the mean daily temperature inside lies about 5°–6° F above the mean daily temperature outside, because of solar heat trapped by the building and heat produced by the occupants and their activities. Shades and reflectivity of outer surfaces reduce this discrepancy somewhat; but the chief effect of insulation is to reduce the daily swing about the mean, and to delay the time of peak load. If the limits of 70°–75° F are taken as desirable inside, then heating is necessary when the outside mean daily temperature falls below 65° F and cooling when it rises above 70° F.

Cooling equipment works best if it operates a large part of the time, so that the water which is condensed has little chance to re-evaporate into the room air. The peak load on the equipment comes, not near noon, but six to ten hours later in a well-built house with relatively thick walls. (In a more lightly built house the time lag will be less.) The realization of these facts has led to the development of air-conditioning units which are smaller but operate more efficiently than those customarily used some years ago.

The cooling equipment required for an average house in New Orleans may be $1,750. This represents 54 per cent of the average annual wage in the United States. The heating equipment required for an average house in Detroit costs about half of this. Operating costs of heating and cooling are hard to compare, since they depend, not only on the initial fuel costs, manufacturing, and distribution charges, but also upon the form in which the energy is used by the unit. Operating costs of cooling are hard to compare from place to place because of the great variation in charges at various points on the supply system. Nevertheless, a compilation of Figures (page 116) suggests that, in general, cooling costs in a hot climate are of the same order as heating costs in a cold climate.

The extent to which the inhabitants of many hot countries can afford to meet such costs is, of course, another question. It is possible, however, that some of the surplus labor in densely

Comparative Operating Costs—House of 1000-1200 Sq. Ft.

	Detroit	Singapore	New Orleans
Heating, degree-days	6580	—	1208
Cooling, degree-days	430	4030	1519
Fuel cost—¢ per therm	9.5	—	5.1
Power cost—¢ per kw-h	2.56	0.75	1.9
Cooling, operating hours	638	6470	1834
Heating cost	$123.90	—	$ 18.10
Cooling cost	39.88	$116.63	122.00
Total cost	$163.78	$116.63	$140.10

populated countries may be gradually turned to the production of air-conditioning equipment, but this would have to be judged in the light of claims for labor in other manufacturing industries, and the relative significance of the products for the local economy.

During the last ten years there has been a rapid increase in the endorsement and acceptance of air-conditioning in the tropics. This endorsement has been not only by individuals who are considering their own comfort, but also by architects and employers of labor, both governmental and private. The desire for air-conditioning is not based upon scientific proof of its value but rather upon the simple idea of comfort when living and working in an atmosphere of "controlled weather." With freedom from pollen, control of temperature, humidity, and air movement, a set of conditions is attained which gives the individual a feeling of "well being." Perhaps it is not biological, perhaps it is only psychological. Be that as it may be, the present situation is a demand by the individual, and the motive or reason seems comfort.

The limiting factor today seems to be the cost of owning and operating air-conditioning plants. As shown in the foregoing comparison of costs in Detroit and Singapore, the fact is clear that relative to the standards of living the residents of the tropics have an expensive appetite.

Perhaps the most spectacular "progress" in the installation of air-conditioning plants has been made by the petroleum industry in the Middle East and the East Indies. No other industry excels the oil industry in speed of technical innovation, and no other industry excels in availability of capital in any currency. The result is that places like Borneo and Yemen, for example, are installing air-conditioning plants on an extensive scale not only for the "imported European" staff but also for the "local" staff. It seems labor, local or imported, cannot be recruited and held otherwise. Whole communities in the Middle East are being air-conditioned. In India the government has gone in for air-conditioning all new buildings as well as converting old ones. Places like Singapore and Leopoldville have come to consider air-conditioning standard in all new buildings.

Whether or not the tropical peoples can afford this is something else again. And no scientific proof has been found as to the ultimate effects. If people sleep well, feel well, and like to live and work in air-conditioned quarters in the hot humid tropics, it would seem to be a net gain in the ultimate economic development of those places.

The foregoing can be summarized by saying the idea is widely accepted and is based on mixed motives; mostly, simple comfort. On the negative side it must be admitted that some critics "don't like" air-conditioning. But here again objective evidence is hard to come by. The present author has, however, gone on record (24c) as favoring a moderate degree of air-conditioning in sleeping quarters and in recreation centers, but otherwise relying upon design to give what climatic protection it can without providing the psychological retreat of cocoon living.

No consideration of tropical housing should pass without mention of the very important part that it plays in sanitation. Disposal of excreta, garbage removal, cleanliness, and disinfestation are important enough in temperate communities; but the price of failure is enormously increased in tropical locations, where flies, mosquitoes, and vermin abound, ready at the least opportunity to spread disease, especially where a considerable segment of the population is inadequately tutored in hygiene. As already stressed, tropical sanitation must first apply all of the hygienic principles of temperate regions, often with much greater emphasis, and then it must take additional special measures to counteract the particular hazards of the region. These measures add not only to the cost of construction, but also to the price that must be paid in vigilance and money to see that the safeguards are preserved at all times.

Social Measures

Since, as was indicated in an earlier section, loss of mental initiative is the most important single direct result of exposure to tropical environments, great significance attaches to any measures which will counter that effect.

This susceptibility of human endeavor in the tropics to psychological influence is not entirely a liability, however. While it is true that certain prevalent conditions tend to intensify the physiological effects in reducing efficiency and output, there are others that have a contrary effect. The latter, moreover, can be reinforced by judicious manipulation of circumstances, and additional spurs to a creative life can be developed. This is no more than modern man has done under other more difficult and more discouraging circumstances. The scene is different, and different methods may be required, but the challenge remains the same.

From the clash of tropical and temperate motivations and habits with respect to activity and provision for future needs, some mode of behavior leading to more rapid tropical development must be developed. Whether by the desire of temperate countries for participation in the resources of the tropics, or by the desire of tropical inhabitants for the technological advances of temperate countries, the destinies of both are rapidly becoming interdependent. So long as the colonial system persisted, the claims of the opposing cultures could be kept ideologically separate, but with the advent of the era of tropical self-development this artificial and temporary solution is no longer feasible. From the complex of patterns, local inhabitants and sojourners from the temperate zones alike must select those which give most promise of physiological satisfaction and economic progress in a community which can ill afford to discriminate between East and West, temperate and tropical, brown and white. As stated by Ralph T. Walker, for example, during a session of the Study Group:

The creation of a sense of "belonging" is just as important for indigenous people as it is for newcomers. The cultural equiva-

lent of the European club is a central feature of many native communities. The possession of individual plots of land for the cultivation of food may serve the dual purpose of improving nutrition
and creating community spirit. The granting of such plots is
likely to be particularly important where laborers are brought
some distance from their native villages to a development project.
Not all will use them, but the granting of plots may have marked
effects upon the labor force.

COMPLICATING FACTORS

As in plant and animal industry, attempts to ameliorate
the effects of tropical climate upon human welfare encounter
many nonclimatic difficulties. The now-familiar triad of ignorance, conservatism, and poverty is at least as potent in
retarding and restricting the improvement of living conditions as it is in throttling agricultural expansion. Fortunately, it is sometimes a little easier to demonstrate the
advantages to be gained in matters of health and to convince
people that a little effort will soon reap rewards, since the
results to be obtained are often more directly discernible. If
a change of habit makes a person feel better, he is likely not
only to continue the new habit but also to encourage his
friends to do likewise. A material demonstration of increased
returns is not always as necessary in winning converts to
healthful practices as it is in gaining support for changing
agricultural practice. The termination of an epidemic or the
saving of a life gravely threatened by an infection may be
enough to win the confidence of an extensive population.
But the expected does not always happen, and the ways of a
reformer can be as hard in this field as elsewhere.

Ignorance

To demonstrate that things can indeed be improved may
invoke great surprise—surprise to the people that it is possible, surprise to the demonstrator that any group could find
it startling. Yet it is perfectly understandable that isolated
and poverty-stricken peasants should be so unknowing. Too
isolated to learn from the outside of advances in the world
at large, and too ill-nourished and starved of hope to devise
bold experiments for themselves, they are doomed to linger

on at a low level of equilibrium with nature or disappear quietly from the scene. It is perhaps difficult for those who take a technological order for granted to imagine such a state of affairs; yet it would not be impossible to find some small groups close to this condition, even in this country— or at least until very recently. In areas where communication is sparse, living precarious, and time for contemplation practically nonexistent, ignorance is at once both the natural result and the cause of the conditions.

Those few who feel that improvement is necessary may be completely unaware of how to secure it. A small group of people, living on the verge of existence, cannot afford to experiment; and in any case they hardly constitute a statistical sample. Experiment is more likely to lead them to irretrievable disaster than to a brave new future. In larger backward groups, the inertia of tradition may entirely outweigh the slight advantage to be gained from the chance of numbers.

A special type of ignorance which is of particular significance in world affairs today is the tendency of some peoples to live virtually in a fool's paradise. In different ways and to different degrees, the Kikuyu, the Fijians, and the Saudi Arabs seek to shut themselves off from the world around and to preserve their ancient forms intact. With such desires one may feel a haunting sympathy, but the hard factual question arises, "How long can they do it?" Whether we or they like it or not, distances are contracting and physical barriers crumbling. The technological world is already knocking at the door; sooner or later the door will open. Those who are not psychologically prepared to adjust themselves to the invading complex may find unadjusted life impossible. The day of acquiescence may be postponed, but the process will be made all the more difficult thereby. It seems necessary for those who are already part of the spreading culture to ease the inevitable transition, either by present persuasion or by preparation for rendering aid in the difficult situations to come.

Conservatism

The fear of novelty, which is the natural cloak of the

uninformed and ill-equipped, is reinforced by several variously operating factors in different places. Where power or wealth is concentrated in the hands of a few, it is perfectly natural that those few will want to preserve present arrangements and will regard any suggestion of radical change with a jaundiced eye. It matters little whether the power is exerted through law, economic control, or religious edict; the effect will be the same. If ways can be found of improving human welfare without greatly disturbing the distribution of power, and if the virtual rulers can be convinced of this, progress should not be too long delayed. But if the power itself is a chief cause or buttress of the undesirable state, considerable patience may be necessary before the natural course of events opens the way for improvement.

It must be admitted that sad experience may have prejudiced some nontechnological peoples against the gift-bearing West. Too often has high-minded evangelism opened the way for less scrupulous exploitation, and one can hardly blame the people of many countries for being suspicious, if not of our present motives and favors, at least of what might come later. For this there is no ready answer and no quick solution; we can merely reiterate our convictions and attempt to provide safeguards for the future.

A more subtle but, perhaps, just as effective resistance may stem from the different sets of cultural values entertained by those we seek to help. Improved health, longer life, and greater productive capacity seem unquestionably good to us; but the happiness of the moment or the good to be gained in some future life may be more important to others.

A woman brought me an ailing child and that started it. That first morning I examined and treated four children with temperatures that ranged from 101.5° to 105.6° with the thermometer under the arm. I was afraid that the 105.6° baby was almost dead. Her eyes were glued shut with infection.

I am not a medical doctor, but I had a good assortment of drugs. I tried to tell the Indians how ill this child was, for I didn't want to be blamed for her death. The mother only stared at me like a frightened animal, but when I measured the antibiotic powder, she mixed it with her breast milk, and we fed it to the baby from a gourd spoon.

Within 24 hours, the temperature of the sickest child was normal, and her mother had bathed and fed her. Only one baby boy still registered 101.5°, and he too seemed to be improving toward the end of my visit with treatments for dysentery and malaria.

My "miracle drugs" aroused only a quiet gratitude in the mothers. Something else, to my surprise, brought a far warmer response. . . . "Your village is one of the prettiest places I have ever seen," I told Tah-Koo-Mah, "and I like your people very much!"

He could not conceal his pleasure. Nor could the others to whom I saw him shortly relay the compliment with forced casualness.[1]

The example may be primitive, but unexpected values will be found in far more complex cultures. The way of a cultural ambassador is perplexing; but if he is a good ambassador he will have more than one demonstration with which to promote his mission.

Poverty

The grinding poverty prevailing in large segments of many tropical populations is too well known to need elaboration. For those who doubt, even a casual glance at the economic statistics compiled by United Nations agencies will be sufficiently compelling evidence. The origins of this poverty are complex, as are the circumstances which perpetuate it. Overpopulation is obviously an important factor today in India, China, and certain other areas of Southeast Asia, as it is in Puerto Rico; but it cannot be said to be a ruling factor in most Central and South American countries, where underpopulation may be a more fitting description. Within any one country family size is usually inversely related to economic status; but no one has really settled the argument as to which is cause and which effect. Ignorance, lack of communications, and conservatism produce and are produced by poverty. The maldistribution of capital and sequestration of land are certainly involved in many areas, as has been pointed out in connection with agriculture. Adherence to antiquated and inefficient methods in the face of

[1] E. Weyer, "Assignment Amazon," *Natural History*, v. 62, (1953), p. 456.

competition by the outside world adds its quota to the
burden; and in some regions past exploitation has removed
a possible source of sorely needed finance with which to right
the balance. Be the causes what they may, the difficulties
placed by poverty in the way of improved living are tremendous indeed and must be fully acknowledged by those who
would have tropical countries apply what is so clearly known
in matters of self-improvement.

"Feed-back" of Socio-economic Conditions

Climate undoubtedly has an important effect, both directly and indirectly, upon economic development. Yet the
economic situation, and the larger group of cultural conditions of which it is a part, also modifies in turn the significance of climatic effects, the way in which the effects are
exerted, and sometimes even the incidence of the climatic
factors themselves.

This "feed-back" relationship is as important to the effects
of climate upon man as it is to agriculture and technology.
Unaccustomed to much discomfort, the new arrival from a
prosperous, temperate-zone country, is apt to find the stress
of a tropical environment most unwelcome, unless he can
escape into a technologically contrived shell of air-conditioning. At the other extreme, the semistarved, disease-ridden,
slum dweller is in no position to meet the physiological demands of heat regulation and have any reserve with which
to be an efficient producer. In between these two extremes
are those whose general health and cultural adaptation are
well suited to the existing conditions, and in whom productive efficiency can come closest to the levels accepted as desirable in temperate climes.

Insofar as the direct effect of climate upon physiological
efficiency is concerned, the socio-economic situation makes
itself felt most markedly through the possibilities it provides
for the technological control of the environment. Even in its
more primitive forms, culture provides a measure of control
through the fashioning of shelter and clothing (32). Indeed,
the control thus provided is sometimes superior to that given
by the cherished practices of higher civilizations. Polynesian
housing and Arab clothing illustrate many of the protective

principles that we, with our scientific advances, have formu-ulated but recently. The one marked improvement that temperate-zone civilizations have been able to add—air-conditioning—is of very recent origin; and, like so many of our discoveries, it is not one which can be applied indiscriminately.

Upon the relationship between climate and psychological efficiency socio-economic factors naturally have a profound effect. The highly motivated individual, whatever his particular incentives may be, will frequently continue not only to operate, but to operate efficiently, under conditions which the poorly motivated person may find unacceptable. This effect was clearly discernible among troops engaged in jungle operations during World War II; and it helps to explain the well-known dissatisfaction so commonly exhibited by officers' wives (civilian as well as military) who are prohibited by social taboos from conducting any domestic work in colonial-type areas. As noted earlier, the socio-economic conditions can be so managed that they work in favor of adaptation instead of against it, but this takes understanding, wisdom, and resolution. The idea that man, who is physiologically a tropical animal, does not "do well" in the tropics, even when infectious disease is controlled and adequate nutrition ensured, is very largely tied up with a failure to realize that civilization, as we speak of it, is a product of temperate climates and must be modified before it can induce optimum efficiency in a tropical setting.

In the transmission of infectious disease social conditions are all-important. To be sure, the climate is most favorable to the development of pathogenic agents and to the flourishing of their animal vectors (mosquitoes, flies, lice, rats, etc.); but it is the socio-economic state which provides the reservoir of untreated, or even untreatable, humanity in which the pathogens are maintained and from which they pass into fresh cycles of infection. The flourishing of animal vectors in the kindly climate, moreover, is certainly not discouraged by a community which is too poor or too apathetic to take strong preventive measures.

While it is true that climate may in some measure work against a high level of nutrition, socio-economic factors multiply those effects enormously to produce the widespread malnutrition found in most tropical countries. The list of such influential factors is long, but poor agricultural technology, inadequate transportation facilities, sequestration of land, undercapitalization, cultural taboos, and irresponsible land ownership rank high among them. The relative importance of these different factors and the interactions between them vary from place to place; mostly, they constitute a formidable combination in which the effects of climate itself become almost negligible. Man has done wondrously well in conquering the physical world; but he has much to learn and still more to achieve in regulating his social environment.

REQUIRED ACTION

For purposes of discussion, it is convenient to consider the problem of what to do under four headings; but again, any subdivision is arbitrary and should not be taken to imply that independent operations can ever be adequate. Human welfare is far too complex to yield to sporadic or uncoordinated effort; in fact, better integrated action rather than just more action is often what is wanted. Prevention of disease, climatic protection, education, and research are closely interdependent and merge with countless other considerations not specifically named; nevertheless, they seem to be convenient headings under which to review the actions which are most necessary in helping man to counter the direct and indirect effects of warm climates upon his welfare.

Disease Prevention

All of the measures known to medical science for reducing the incidence of infectious disease in the tropics need to be vigorously applied wherever the need appears. Destruction of vectors, control of their breeding sites, prevention of their access to sources of infection, removal or segregation of disease reservoirs, suppression of infectious agents in the patient or host, and immunization of susceptible persons, singly and in combination, constitute a formidable threat to tropical disease when rigorously applied. But they must be rigorously applied under the local conditions, many of which offer special difficulties. Illiteracy and lack of technical skill greatly affect the handling of the problem.

Administrative procedures must be adapted to the circumstances. In the United States, the top administrative staff would be engaged in substantive tasks, but in the tropics they are often taken up with supervisory duties. The particular operation must be broken down into its component parts, of course, and each part taught separately to the personnel who will carry it out. But all this will collapse and perhaps do more harm than good unless close and constant supervision is maintained over the detailed execution of the work. For effective work, moreover, sanitary operations must be carried out on a big scale; often on a continuously expanding scale. Clearing mosquitoes from a small area has little effect if new hordes swarm in from the surrounding regions. Quarantine is a costly and uncertain barrier against the introduction of disease from a surrounding infected area. Air transportation is increasing the dangers even for those countries surrounded by wide seas or deserts. World-wide elimination, indeed, must be the final objective.

Preventive measures have reached a high degree of efficiency and are often applicable at comparatively low cost. But it must not be assumed that the Augean stables can be swept clean this easily. The ecological cycle of one disease cannot be abolished, or even seriously disturbed, without profound effects upon still wider ecological patterns. As one infective agent is subdued, another may spring into prominence; as one vector is eliminated, another may take its place—or, as too frequently happens, the small percentage of vectors resistant to the particular mode of attack, freed from competition with their fellows, may build up a formidable population equally effective in carrying disease, but undeterred by the measure which promised elimination of the vector. Furthermore, reduction, let alone elimination, of a disease creates new problems. Those whose lives have been spared must now be fed, clothed, housed, and employed. They also swell the numbers left to suffer other, as yet uncontrolled, diseases. In a country which is underpopulated in relation to its resources, distinct gains are almost certain; but in areas where overpopulation is already a serious matter, the benefits of a program which stops at saving lives are apt to become nebulous.

The endeavor to lessen morbidity and mortality from "preventable" disease must go on, of course; but it must be conducted with all the wisdom that sober reflection suggests and with a due regard for the possible ultimate consequences of a massive interference with the biological balance hitherto existing and, in particular, the necessity for providing food and a livelihood for those who are saved.

Climatic Protection

Clothing can ward off marauding insects and abrading vegetation, as well as satisfy social conventions. Insofar as the heat is concerned, however, it is apt to be a liability. The problem is to obtain the essential benefits of clothing without interfering with heat loss. In this respect, native peoples are often ahead of the culture-bound immigrants, and the chief need is for education of those who know only temperate customs.

Housing, by contrast, may offer real climatic protection. But here again there are many cultural problems. Extreme positions are often taken with imported customs on the one hand, and native practices on the other; but it is not always the newly arrived or temporary inhabitant who clings tenaciously to the less adapted pattern. In many rural areas of Latin America, for example, the thick-walled, shuttered, ill-ventilated structure designed for the arid conditions of Iberia will be found yielding only reluctantly and very recently to light, open, and breeze-inviting designs so much better suited to continuously warm and humid environments. Some of the more important considerations are given in the following summary of comments made by Ralph T. Walker:

It is important to provide adequate housing for people imported from temperate zones, first because such people are and will continue for some time to be essential to the technological aspects of development, second because the practices and living standards so introduced will help to stimulate the indigenous peoples to emulation, thirdly because the housing provided in this way will be available to indigenous technologists as they develop. For these reasons, also, it is advisable to think in terms of permanent housing right from the first beginnings of the construction camp. The supposed economy of temporary housing usually turns out to be illusory, and the social blight imposed by it unjustifiable.

In providing housing for such imported families, careful consideration must be given to the desires of the women. Privacy is something in high demand which is difficult to guarantee in lightly constructed, open, tropical dwellings, unless they are widely spaced. Variety in form and decoration is something too often overlooked in the preparation of ground plans. Community amenities—clubs, churches, schools, recreation grounds—are proportionately more important to European-type communities set in tropical isolation.

Protection against climatic elements and the maintenance of comfort in the face of tropical hazards should be sought primarily through design. Mechanical aids to comfort, such as air-conditioning, are best regarded as supplementary—to be used only after everything that can be achieved by design is effected, and only to the extent that they are really necessary. The specific design features to be considered are legion, and vary with the economic situation, the detailed climatic regime, and the materials available. Some of the more interesting features include: support of the house on piles for cooling, termite control, and recreation space; Dutch doors opening on the lee side to give ventilation without draught in the trade-wind belt; floor-level ventilation; roof space ventilation from eaves through ridge ventilators; window shades such as the *solide persienne* and *sol brisé;* and the judicious use of trees.

European-type housing may be available to the wealthier of the local inhabitants, and it will become available to the more skilled native technologists as they take over executive responsibilities. But it is likely to be beyond the reach of the great mass of indigenous peoples for some time to come. In many cases, the established local types of better-class housing are well-adapted to local conditions. There is usually room for improvement in hygienic aspects, as in the disposal of refuse, control of vermin, discouragement of disease vectors, and reduction of crowding. But the basic design is often sound, and may call for change only in details. Temperate technology should not be in a hurry to change the better local types unless there is a strong local demand and the economic situation permits. There are numerous examples of good indigenous practices, such as the combination of thick-walled day and thin-walled night portions in the Cameroons, the open thatched house of Polynesia, and the thick-walled earth dwellings, sometimes with semibasement earth insulation, of Egypt and the Sudan. Some of these features could well be retained, even when more Westernized structures are designed.

The first concern of indigenous people is usually with utilizing easily available material (thatch, small timber, earth), the second with preserving traditional practice, interwoven with sanctions and taboos, into which common experience and superstition enter in complex fashion. Well-being and comfort are much less important considerations in most indigenous cultures and carry little weight in proposals to change local customs—at least until a large measure of "Westernization" has occurred. This native conservatism must be recognized and its better features accepted if the good will of the people is to be enlisted for the introduction of measures essential to health. Unfortunately, when it comes, the breakdown of conservatism is apt to be much too sudden, and sometimes produces bizarre effects. Western advisers then find their role reversed, with their main concern one of restraining enthusiasm for those "Western" items and practices which would not be at all suited to local conditions.

Education

As in most practical endeavors, there is considerable scope for the more extensive application of knowledge that already exists. Much of the available information, especially on the physiological and psychological reactions of man, has not yet found its way into actual operations. In many instances application of the knowledge is blocked by the inevitable inertia of existing practices—an inertia which can be overcome only gradually, unless some chance event gives an opportunity for capturing influential support. In other cases the speed of progress is limited by the cost, by a lack of trained personnel, or by the multiplicity of events that must be co-ordinated before success can attend the effort. These last two impediments are commonly experienced in efforts to control disease or improve nutritional standards.

The delay in getting available knowledge applied to human needs is by no means unique to tropical problems and is not likely to become less as long as the sum of new knowledge continues to accumulate at its present ever-increasing rate. It is a matter of some surprise, indeed, that the art of communication has managed to keep pace at all with the tremendous increase in information. In the circumstances it is advantageous periodically to list those items which call for preferential application, either because they are inherently important or because they are easily done. In connection with human welfare three matters call for more intensive educational effort.

First, more deliberate consideration should be given to providing incentives to activity. In a general sense such incentives will automatically be forthcoming if the economic level is raised; but to move a stuck wheel it is important to apply pressure at all available points. Inducements that appeal to the individual worker, as distinct from those which, however logical, strike him as remote and theoretical, may very well start the motion. Gathering momentum, this will bring in turn the benefits of an improved economy. In the tropics, where various factors combine to diminish incentive, remedial action is even more important than in cooler regions. The planning of incentives calls for an intimate understanding of the individual worker in the particular locality; their presentation calls for imagination. It is unlikely that the streamlined mass psychology so commonly used in temperate-zone countries would be effective in heterogeneous tropical regions.

Second, and often in combination with the first, still greater effort is required in educating the poorer members of tropical communities to the personal advantages of simple sanitation and cooperation with organized public health measures. *Third,* and closely affecting the others, is the need for social evolution toward a less disparate possession of economic return, equal participation in governmental process, and the right to reap the rewards of conscientious endeavor. Only by accelerating the intricate machinery involved in these processes can the restrictive effects of climate upon economic welfare be reduced.

Research

But the application of present knowledge is not enough. While the winning of still more knowledge may intensify the problems of application in some respects, the need for better understanding far outweighs these difficulties. The stream of knowledge does not flow continuously between the confining banks of a single channel; rather, it pours through a complex system of interlacing waterways to intermingle and produce interactive effects that none can clearly predict. Channels may be improved and better use made of the released forces, but there is always a demand for more and still more power to supplement the developments made possible by the earlier flows. Unfortunately, for the hundreds that clamor to use the power, there is scarcely one who will lend his effort or furnish the capital with which to seek new sources, at least without some expectation of fairly immediate returns. The need for better information can be clearly seen on such topics as:

The effect of climatic conditions on comfort and efficiency.
The effect of long exposure to tropical conditions.
The effect and relative importance of nutrition, health, race, economic and social status, tradition, etc., on heat tolerance and efficiency.
The ability to adjust to dietary alterations without loss of efficiency.
The methods of making quantitative assessments of climatic situations; and the effect of climate on infectious disease.

Research, however, has a habit of posing more problems than it answers, so that the field of inquiry widens, and the benefits to be derived from the inquiry increase as we penetrate more and more deeply into it. In view of the short time that systematic research into human welfare has been in existence, it is certain that the ground already broken represents nothing more than limited and superficial scratching of the terrain that awaits development. As new drugs and new biological agents become available for the attack upon the transmission of disease, and as new materials become available for housing, research is necessary not only upon their effectiveness under tropical conditions but also upon the most economical way in which they can be used under those conditions. In fact, there is a great need for continuing research into cost-control of all tropical operations.

PREFERENTIAL REGIONS

If the guide to the distribution of limited effort is to be the utilitarian one of the greatest good for the greatest number, then the region of maximum effectiveness would be one which is already showing signs of improvement, but which is still so affected that further improvement is likely to be attended by good returns. A region which is already well developed might be in the stage of diminishing returns, giving a relatively small additional yield for the effort expended. On the other hand, a region which is in a deplorable state might be expected to show little response unless considerable means were expended.

Practical considerations, however, might cut across this simple consideration of probabilities, and not everyone will accept the utilitarian philosophy. The country already well advanced may represent a considerable past investment, needing a little more to make it permanent, but liable to rapid depreciation in the absence of further assistance. Countries which are in a bad state, on the other hand, present a humanitarian appeal which can hardly be denied.

An overriding consideration in disease prevention is the effectiveness of the cooperation that can be expected from the government and the people concerned. This is particularly true where control must be exercised on a large scale before it can be effective. The strategic location of the area in relation to the war on disease is also a consideration, since it may be more important to clean out the last areas of a disease on a continent than to start a new campaign in a limited portion of a widely affected one. It might be even more important quickly to stamp out new infections in an area hitherto free. The degree of cooperation to be expected is of primary importance also in educational matters, but perhaps more in determining the type of educational effort than its intensity. Research must take the opportunities as they occur or make them as the necessity arises. It is much more difficult to postulate in advance where research should be done, and the difficult problems created by this necessarily opportunistic attitude will be taken up in Chapter 7. Suffice it here to say that regimentation is not the way to get the best out of this temperamental child.

Chapter 6

INDUSTRY

INDUSTRIALIZATION is not synonymous with economic development. Nevertheless, the lack of industry in most tropical countries is a part of their lack of economic development. Some increase in industry, properly selected and related to the resources and needs of the country, and the aptitudes of its people, is a necessary part of development. Our problem is to consider what effect tropical climates may have on the prospects of industrialization.

The lack of industry in the tropics is well known, but it is hard to measure. Table 17 sets out some figures that should be regarded as illustrative rather than exact. They show, for certain countries in and out of the tropics, the value of the output of manufacturing industries minus the sums paid by those industries for raw materials, fuel and power, and certain other items. In the terminology of United Nations statistical offices this is called "net value of production"; it is more familiar to some economists as "value added by manufacture." It measures, roughly, the value of the manufacturing process in each country. For a number of reasons it has been possible to show on the table only a few countries, but there are enough to confirm the broad outlines of "what everybody knows" about the lack of industry in the tropics.

It would not be wise to make a close comparison between countries on the basis of the data given in the table. To start with, there are differences in years, and even in the same year production in a particular country may be abnormally high or low. The industrial censuses on which the output figures are based also vary in coverage; some include only establishments with 20 employees, some use 5 as the limit, some have other standards; the definition of what is manufacturing probably varies. The reliability of the data collected may vary markedly from country to country. Per-

Table 17

INDUSTRIAL PRODUCTION IN CERTAIN COUNTRIES

Value Added by Manufacture

Country	Year	Total (in millions $)	Per capita (in $)
Africa			
Egypt	1954	237.2	10.45
Ethiopia	*1953*	*5.3*	*.35*
Mozambique	*1953*	*12.1*	*2.05*
S. Rhodesia	*1953*	*73.1*	*31.78*
U. of S. Afr.	1951-2	967.7	76.19
Asia			
Burma	*1953*	*31.3*	*1.63*
India	*1952*	*661.5*	*1.85*
Japan	1953	4,704.5	53.45
Latin America			
Chile	1951	263.4	44.64
Peru	*1950*	*65.3*	*7.10*
Mexico	*1953*	*212.6*	*7.38*
Guatemala	*1953*	*23.2*	*7.49*
Puerto Rico	*1952*	*126.5*	*57.50*
Other			
U.S.	1953	121,659.	749.13
Canada	1953	8,127.8	538.26
U.K.	1951	14,126.0	281.39
Australia	1953-54	2,672.3	297.25

Source: U.N. *Statistical Yearbook*, 1955, Tables 1, 67, 159.
Note: Local currencies were converted into U.S. dollars at the following exchange rates, expressed as U.S. cents in local currency units: Egypt 287; Ethiopia 40.3; Mozambique 3.5; Southern Rhodesia and Union of South Africa, 280; Burma and India, 21; Japan 0.278; Chile 1.1; Peru 6.5; Mexico 11.56; Guatemala and Puerto Rico 100; Canada 101.7; U.K. 280; Australia 224.
Population figures used were U.N. estimate for nearest year. See Table 67 of source for coverage of data which differ for many countries.

haps most important of all the factors hampering comparison are price differences. The same number of physical units of production may count for two or three times as much "value added by manufacture" in one country as in another if the prices are that much higher. Add to this the arbitrary elements in many exchange rates during the past ten years and it becomes clear that international comparisons of these data can only be made with the utmost caution. Nevertheless the great differences in magnitude between the countries with the greatest manufacturing output and those with the least, and the tendency for that difference to correspond with the climatic position of countries, shows that in manufacturing, as in most economic activities examined in this book, production in the tropics is generally at a much lower level than in many temperate zone countries.

Certainly climate is not the main determinant of the level of industrial development. In the tropics there are both a Brazil and an Ethiopia, a Nigeria and a Puerto Rico. As in the case of life expectancy and infant mortality (Table 13), factors other than climate must be largely responsible for differences within the tropics, although climate may act adversely on all of them as against the temperate zones.

THE EFFECTS OF CLIMATE

As a youth in Australia, the author frequently heard it said that the country's climate was unsuitable for weaving textiles or manufacturing steel; at a more mature age he learned that it was also supposed to affect the quality of the beer. Some years later he witnessed considerable success attending both the textile and the steel industry and came to believe that the principal effect of climate upon brewing was through the thirst induced in the inhabitants. In industry, as in biology, the facts of climatic effect need to be distinguished from the fiction. Climate undoubtedly does affect many industrial operations, but progress will not be served by hasty generalizations, or by making decisions in the name of climate which are actually dictated by quite other considerations. A few of the leading ways in which climate might influence industrial operations in the tropics will be considered here, but a critical examination is needed over a much wider field before one can deal realistically with this aspect of economic development.

On Transportation

For many the word "tropics" suggests a strip of perpetual mud, twisting its way through dripping jungle, dotted with hopelessly bogged vehicles, and skirted by weary peasants carrying on their backs those goods which cannot await the passing of the monsoon. For others the picture is rather that of a narrow road precariously cut in the hillside, intersected by mountain torrents and ravaged by landslides, and imposing repeated and indeterminate delays upon communications. That these are reflections of reality, none can deny; but they do not represent the whole truth.

Rains are heavy, soils are of clay, erosion is high. But road-making is often primitive, commerce has not been such as to impel improvement, and alternative methods are sometimes available. When one attempts to impose technological operations upon a system developed for a more leisurely economy, one must expect difficulties. The possibility of effecting some adjustment will be discussed shortly, but at this point we should realize that nature sometimes helps as well as hinders by providing magnificent waterways, and through them a cheap, though slow, method of transportation. This is particularly true in the northeastern part of South America, and some regions of Southeast Asia. Unfortunately, the gift is qualified in the Congo River by the numerous rapids which interrupt its course. The regions presenting the greatest difficulties for transportation are those where mountains lie athwart the desired communications, as in much of Central America, the western part of South America, and many areas of Southeast Asia. In these regions the terrain itself must share the responsibility with climate. Air transportation, the modern answer to earth-bound difficulties, does not entirely escape climatic opposition in the form of dense clouds, turbulent atmospheres, and treacherous landing grounds; but it is an open question whether these hazards are any worse than those presented by many temperate climes.

On Deterioration of Materials

The causes of deterioration were described by Wessel at our conference under three main headings: physical, chemical and biological; but he was careful to point out that they are not specific to the tropics. (See also item 16 in the bibliography.) All can and do operate in temperate climates, although certain of the causative factors are either more intense in the tropics or are assisted by the climatic conditions. The most important factors appear to be heat, sunlight, moisture, oxygen and ozone, and biological agents. Clear-cut cases of deterioration caused by a single destructive factor are rarely if ever found. Almost all cases are complicated by having two or more causative factors functioning simultaneously.

Temperature variations modify the physical properties of almost all known materials and have a direct bearing on the rate of a wide variety of chemical reactions. There is considerable variation in the ability of materials to absorb, conduct, radiate, and reflect heat. Under the same irradiation dark-colored substances of low conductivity tend to become hotter than white substances of high conductivity.

Rises in temperature increase the natural tendency of many substances to deteriorate. Thus, heat adds its effects to those of sunlight, oxygen, ozone, and moisture in breaking down polymeric substances such as natural and synthetic plastics, rubbers, textiles, leather, and paper. Alternate expansion and contraction of materials due to variations in temperature may impose strains leading to deterioration in physical properties.

Sunlight, especially the short-wavelength ultraviolet, when absorbed and of sufficient activity, is considered to account for widespread destruction of materials and equipment. Acting alone or in conjunction with moisture, oxygen, and ozone, photochemical reactions do great damage to plastics, rubber, textiles, and coatings.

In general, the susceptibility of textile fibres to sunlight deterioration is, in decreasing order: silk, jute, rayon, cotton, flax, hemp, raw wool, and chromed wool. Coarse yarns are more resistant than fine. Dull nylon has only slightly better resistance than silk, whereas bright nylon approaches the resistance of cotton. Saran is only slightly affected, velon darkens slightly. Cellulose acetate is more sensitive than cuprammonium or viscose rayons. The acrylonitrile fibres, orlon and chemstrand, are remarkably resistant. Dacron is thought to possess good resistance. . . . A number of synthetic rubbers are more resistant to sunlight aging than is natural rubber. A point of interest with regard to sunlight deterioration of elastomeric compounds is the fact that the effects are always more pronounced on stretched or sharply bent specimens than on relaxed samples. (16)

Moisture in the liquid and vapor states acts in both a physical and a chemical capacity to promote deterioration. The cohesion of paper is often destroyed, and a brown line becomes apparent in certain textiles once they have become wet. Paint and lacquer films tend to crack and blister. Absorbent materials, such as wood and wood products, swell and shrink with the relative humidity of the atmosphere, with consequent warping and cracking, as well as the creation of tensions in attached structures. Corrosion of metals, a tremendously important and costly problem, is facilitated by moisture and accelerated by high temperatures. Moisture has a particularly important effect on the operation of electrical and, especially, electronic equipment.

Micro-organisms, as we have seen, are abundant in tropical regions, and find in the guaranteed humidity an excellent medium for growth and propagation. "The temperature optima for many fungi lie in the range of 15° to 30° C, but fungi of one sort or another have been found to grow from as low as 0° C to as high as 50° C. Relative humidity is important in determining growth of fungi. Below 70% relative humidity there is little opportunity for fungal growth; many forms grow well at 80 to 95%; and above 95% relative humidity the fungi flourish." (16) The higher relative humidities occur whenever the air temperature falls toward the dew point, usually at night, or where there is insufficient air movement to dry a damp surface. Both conditions are likely to occur in storage places. Micro-organisms cause deterioration of industrial materials by actual consumption of the substrate such as cellulosic constituents of wood, cotton, and paper; by defacement and staining as on painted surfaces; or by reaction of their metabolic chemical end-products with substrates such as metals and glass. Where the micro-organisms infect human food the further dangers arise that toxic substances may be produced, or that the organisms themselves may become parasitic in the body. Few materials are proof against the attack of micro-organisms in the tropics. Textiles, wood, paper, leather, plastics, optical equipment, electrical apparatus, glass, and concrete may all suffer.

Of the various insects which may attack industrial materials, two groups are pre-eminent: the "powder-post" beetles, and the termites. In each group there are numerous genera and species, each with its own favorite target and each with its own pattern of optimum conditions. While wood is most commonly ravaged by these pests, such different and even unlikely materials as asphalt, asbestos, bitumen and lead coverings may be pierced when they block passage to desirable food. By no means unknown in more temperate regions, these insects nevertheless find optimum conditions in most tropical areas, where they constitute a perpetual and serious economic threat, especially to the somewhat less durable materials that are normally employed in construction.

The activities of rodents are certainly no less in tropical than in temperate climates, so that the damage done by them must be reckoned in the total of deteriorative processes, although it would be fairer to ascribe their predation to the unhygienic and crowded dwellings than to climate per se. The same can be said about roaches, crickets, grasshoppers, clothes moths, carpet beetles, silver fish and the like, which, though common in the tropics, are by no means strangers to the temperate zones.

On Industrial Processes

Obviously, from what was said in the chapter on human health and efficiency, one must expect to encounter certain difficulties in the hot and heavy industries by reason of reduced efficiency in the workers, and even a certain diminution of reliability and spontaneity in management and administration. But consideration must also be given to the effect of climate upon the industrial processes themselves. If rapid and fairly complete drying is necessary at some stage of the manufacture, for example, then difficulties or failures will develop under the relatively moist conditions of the tropics. Or if machinery is designed to operate with plastic components having the degree of rigidity found in temperate climates, malfunctioning may occur with the softer and more flexible items on hot days. Waxes, fats, and lubricants require a higher melting point if they are to be satisfactory under higher temperatures. Lacquers are likely to give a cloudy and imperfect finish if applied when the humidity is high, and some adhesives may lose their tenacity. Most of these effects, however, can be countered with a little ingenuity and do not constitute a serious bar to industrialization once the necessity for adjustment is recognized. Processes which require a high temperature or a high humidity, on the other hand, may actually be easier where tropical nature assists. The so-called "drying" of oil finishes may take place more rapidly, and spinning of fibres might call for very little alteration of the prevailing humidity.

On Power Supply

The annual input to the world energy system from water power now amounts to about 0.7 per cent of the total system requirement. The actual input continues to increase, but the rate of growth has been declining. If the decline . . . does not carry the rate of growth below one per cent at the end of a hundred years, then the input from water power would have increased about 5-fold by A.D. 2000 and about 17-fold by A.D. 2050. (38)

This is not a very exciting picture for the world as a whole, but one might expect that a major portion of the untapped water power is in those parts of the tropics where rainfall is high and slopes are steep. The tropical areas of Africa have a high potential, those of the Americas a moderate potential, those of the Australo-Asian region a low potential. For the utilization of water power, continuity of flow is important. This means either that the rainfall should be evenly distributed over the year or that reservoirs will be required with a capacity great enough to carry industry through the dry periods. Many tropical areas have a seasonal rainfall and rugged terrain which offers little inducement to the construction of reservoirs. Nevertheless, there is in water power a certain promise for future development.

The feasibility of capturing solar energy is more conjectural. Putnam states that one square foot of pipe-absorber-glass area will produce a gallon of 180° F water daily during seven or eight months of the year in Miami, Florida (38). But even in rural areas, where there are no washing machines, average demands for hot water are about 100 gallons per day for a family of five. The cost in the United States of solar water heating is rather less than that of electrical heating, but twice that of oil heating, four times that of coal heating, and over five times that of heating by natural gas. A low-cost ($14) solar cooker developed in India, which takes about twenty minutes to prepare a standard Indian meal of lentils and rice, seems practical however. On the subject of distillation of fresh water from brine, however, Putnam is pessimistic: "Solar stills appear to be economically obsolete, at least for the present. Costs of about $15 an acre-foot have been claimed for the ion-exchange method. It is difficult to see how solar distillation can produce fresh water for much less than $100 an acre-foot."

The subject of solar energy was freely discussed, and exhibits of actual utilization were displayed, at an International Conference and Symposium on Applied Solar Energy, held in Arizona in 1955 (1b). Solar energy can be used in many ways: in cookers, stills, space heaters, refrigerators, heat engines, photosynthetic production of food or organic reagents, photovoltaic conversion to electric power, or furnaces. I feel, however, that the conference established as much the limitations of solar energy conversion as it highlighted the few spectacular developments. Solar furnaces provide a new and, in some respects, unique tool for research and for special chemical processes; new "solar batteries" arising out of transistor research, and already showing eleven per cent efficiency in conversion, have practical promise; and a hypothetical plant for conversion of algal products to industrial fuels provides a stimulating new vision. But the remaining uses appear to have importance only where conventional forms of energy are unobtainable or very expensive, or where they can be combined with some other form of intermittent power supply, such as wind. Eventually, solar power will fade into insignificance as compared with nuclear power, but in the meantime it may help in some degree to put more motion in the economic wheel of certain underdeveloped tropical countries.

The following extract will serve to introduce a provocative thought for future planners:

Along some, but not all, tropical coasts, the hot surface water is closely underlain by cold water. . . . Such differences between "limitless" masses of water suggest that great quantities of energy could be obtained from the relatively high thermal potential. Georges Claude made the first attempt to obtain this energy in 1930 off Havana. His apparatus was wrecked by a gale. The French Government is trying again, off the Gold Coast [actually Ivory Coast] of West Africa, near Abidjan. Two 3500 kilowatt units are planned. Components were successfully tested full-scale in the sea off Marseilles in September, 1947. . . . The French consider that the potential economies of thermal sea energy compare favorably with much land-borne hydro. But suitable sites close to storm-free tropical coasts with cold water not too deep and not too far off shore, and close to load centers, are not as common as are hydroelectric sites. Perhaps, over the next 100 years, we might hope for one-tenth as much energy from temperature differences of the sea as from hydro, requiring an installed capacity of a hundred million kilowatts or so. (38)

CIRCUMVENTING EFFECTS

Whenever the effect of tropical climates upon some phase of economic development is broached, the discussion tends to run off into considerations of the economic development itself, leaving the original question of the climatic role unanswered. In topics dealt with in previous chapters—crop production, animal production, and human health and efficiency—it is usually possible to steer the discussion back to the main question; but in the field of industrial development this proves difficult. One gets the impression that the difficulty arises here, not so much because climate is unimportant or because too little is known about its effects, but because at the present juncture there are so many other and more potent factors interfering with industrial development. Nevertheless, reduction of climatic effects is of some importance, even now, and will become relatively more important as the nonclimatic difficulties are surmounted.

Modification of Methods

In a community of high technology a normal method of meeting environmental interference is by controlling the environment; but in a country unused to such procedures, where control may be both difficult and expensive, some compromise may be much more practical. Altogether apart from climatic effect, methods will almost certainly need modification. Differences in raw materials, in manual skills, in motivations, and in markets will call for considerable alterations in both design and operation of most processes from those prevailing in temperate countries. The incorporation of modifications to meet climatic conditions as well should not be too onerous. Indeed, it is not inconceivable that through the attention given to making such modifications the whole process may be improved. A change in stacking may permit better drying; modification of a solvent, a better finish; alteration of annealing procedures, a more durable product. The substitution of materials may not only remove the manufacturing difficulty but also give an end product more suited to local conditions or more cheaply made from local materials. Industry advances as much by facing its threats as by walling them off.

Vehicles have been modified for negotiating mud and climbing slippery slopes. Usually though, they render the way completely impassable to anything not similarly equipped and earn the ire of the less fortunate inhabitants. Air transportation is coming to supplement surface routes more and more, but it will be a long time before it can carry goods other than those with a high economic or strategic priority.

Climatic Protection

Insofar as difficulties cannot be met by adaptation, the exclusion of the interfering climatic factor should be con-

sidered. Dehumidification may be essential where high relative humidities or high vapor pressures interfere with an
important operation. Cooling may be necessary for the manipulation of plastic materials or biological reagents. Sunlight may need to be dimmed for the preservation of reference colors or other light-sensitive materials. Screening and
filtering would be required if air-borne articles or insects are
damaging to the processes. To the extent that such special
precautions are necessary, air-conditioning for human comfort may be included as well. Indeed, industry offers the
greatest opportunity to the development of air-conditioning.
Relative to other capital costs, the expense of installation is
apt to be small; the investment will be profitable where the
process is critical; and the work force is contented, to boot.

Preservatives can be used to protect materials against
micro organisms, where cooling or drying by air-conditioning is not practicable. The list of preservatives is continually increasing as newer and more efficacious compounds
are devised and as the number of materials that require protection grows. But, as usual, care has to be taken that the
material is not spoiled in other ways or that the preservative
is not harmful to man or animals that may come into contact
with it. Hardwoods and even some soft woods can be protected against termites, cellulose materials can be given better resistance to fungal damage, and the corrosion of metals
can be reduced. Protection is seldom complete or permanent,
however, and constant inspection is necessary to ensure continued life.

Weather Wisdom

In some parts of the tropics there is little variation in rainfall or other climatic conditions throughout the year. In
Singapore, April is by courtesy the "dry" month, since it rains
only every third instead of every second day. But in many
large regions there are distinct dry and wet seasons, well
known to the inhabitants, who arrange their activities
around this annual cycle. Industry might well follow the
same pattern, much as it used to do in colder countries, and
reserve critical processes for the season most favorable to
them.

Where fluctuations, rather than distinct seasons, characterize the weather, the thought occurs that it may be possible to link industrial activity to weather forecasts, as is done in marketing and other matters in this country. But the prospect is not very reassuring. There are distinct limitations to the reliability of weather predictions even here, where reporting stations are very numerous and weather fronts usually well marked. In the tropics, where the network of stations is more tenuous and fronts are indistinct, one could hardly expect a very reliable estimate.

COMPLICATING FACTORS

In previous chapters we have been able to establish very definite and important influences of tropical climate upon crop production, animal husbandry, and the general sweep of human welfare and productivity; and in discussing palliative measures we have had to refer to various nonclimatic factors which may affect the success or practicability of those measures. This was possible without losing sight of the main topic—the role of climate. But when it comes to a discussion of industry, the evidence for direct and important climatic effects is somewhat insubstantial, and a consideration of nonclimatic influences is apt to develop into a full-fledged discussion of the socio-economic forces necessary to the process of industrialization. Nevertheless, industrial development has been widely advocated as a panacea for the economic ills of the tropics, and, like any other human activity, it is tied to all circumstances which affect man himself. Some brief consideration of the nonclimatic factors which influence industrialization seems justified, therefore, if a rounded picture is to be obtained.

Tropical countries probably produce about one-third of the free world's industrial raw materials. Agricultural products furnish a large part of these raw materials, animal products a small fraction. But a considerable and increasing part is derived from mining and drilling operations. Iron ore, bauxite, tin, manganese, and petroleum are outstanding and familiar examples. The volume of such raw materials readily available in the tropics greatly exceeds the present local capacity for conversion into finished products. In this respect, therefore, the tropics as a whole are far from being unfavorably placed industrially, although the assets are somewhat unevenly distributed between countries. Many areas are lacking in certain supplementary materials, such as coal, but this deficiency may be compensated by water power and, at least temporarily, timber for fuel.

It is evident that many countries are impeded in their quest for improved living conditions by a marked shortage of capital. In countries with an excess of population relative to resources, the accretion of capital by savings is both difficult and slow. In those that are underpopulated, national overhead is burdensome. There is no unanimity on either the diagnosis of the specific cause or the most appropriate remedy to be applied in many areas, and their discussion is not warranted here; but the situation undoubtedly interferes seriously with the adaptation of industrial procedures to tropical circumstances.

The supply of labor may present an equally difficult problem. A superabundance of extremely poor people does not necessarily provide a work force. Undernourishment, disease, lack of education, lack of ambition, or ingrained custom, singly or in combination, may make of the apparent plenitude a veritable mirage. Public health measures and education may, in time, rectify the position, but they must be paid for and presumably treated as an investment in future productivity.

Nor would the tropical paradise be complete when it had natural resources, capital for development, and a potential work force. Production will not be stimulated unless there is an adequate outlet for the product. Markets must be in sight; and access to markets is affected by many things, some local and tropical, such as sheltered harbors or airfields, others remote and far from climatic. Countless failures, large and small, from the South Sea Bubble to the East African Groundnut Scheme, testify to the complexity of tropical development and the need for a clear consideration of hard realities.

Perhaps one of the most powerful restrictions upon the rate of industrial development is the general need for balance. Rarely can one special industry develop without both requiring and promoting parallel evolution in other aspects. Practically every industry requires power, which in turn means acquiring fuel or harnessing energy and transmitting it to the point of use. Raw materials must be brought in, or products taken out, over roads, rivers, rail, or by air; and this in turn calls for adequate vehicles, ports, and handling facilities. Workers must be fed, clothed, housed, and provided with recreation. Families require schooling, stores, and services. Communications by mail, telephone, telegraph, or radio must be installed. Contact with the outside world creates new desires, engenders new problems, calls for new adjustments. Unless both management and labor are psychologically prepared for these developments, and unless the material resources are available for their realization, progress can at best be but intermittent and uncertain, especially in a climate which detracts from initiative and obstructs fruition.

REQUIRED ACTION

Enough has been said in the preceding section to indicate the wide variety of nonclimatic factors that may influence the course of industrialization in the tropics. It will be well to confine ourselves here to a review of those actions which would be necessary to counter the more strictly climatic difficulties, bearing always in mind the total situation.

Transportation

As we have seen, transportation is important not only for the industry itself, but also for the ancillary developments that must attend industrial growth. It would appear reasonable, therefore, to urge that it be planned on a wide basis, giving consideration to all forms of transportation and all phases of development. The relative merits of road, rail, river, and air carriage can then be examined in relation to the environmental factors of climate and terrain, each being used to the extent that it best fits the circumstances and all being developed in a co-ordinated fashion. Roads need to be sited with due regard for soil stability, watercourses, and contours, and to be laid with greater care for foundations, drainage, and flood protection than is usually taken in the absence of industrial stimulus. Railroads require even greater consideration for gradients, bridges, landslides, and washaways. River transportation raises the problem of dredging, flood control, landings, and handling facilities in locations where deterioration is rapid and approaches are difficult. Air freight immediately brings up questions of cost, maintenance of airports, and flight control.

For none of these transportation problems is there likely to be a categorical answer. A painstaking survey will usually be required to obtain the facts essential to a decision; and the decision itself can be made only after the various aspects of practicability, cost, and reliability have been thoroughly reviewed. A wide variety of expert technical assistance will usually be necessary both for the survey and for the final analysis. There is scarcely a scientific discipline from anthropology to zoology that will not need to be consulted in the process. To cut corners or take risks in this matter could be disastrous. It may well transpire that the whole question of establishing an industry hinges on the feasibility of providing adequate transportation over difficult terrain.

Preservation

There are no reliable figures on deterioration losses in the tropics, but in the nontropical United States the annual loss runs to $12 billion (16). This loss is almost entirely preventible; the question is whether the cost of prevention is substantially less. Again, this is something to which no categorical answer can be given. It would seem reasonable to suppose that the cost would be well repaid in certain cases. Termite-proofing of structural timbers costs relatively little in comparison with replacing them in a completed structure. The addition of small heating lamps to electrical equipment to prevent condensation is obviously worthwhile. Weatherproof paints are clearly necessary for soft woods. But the wholesale treatment of textiles with fungicide may be quite out of the question. With sufficient forethought, the three basic preventive principles—selecting resistant materials, adding preservatives against biological agents, and reducing moisture content—can be followed, each where it is most appropriate in terms of effectiveness and cost. But forethought is necessary, and basic to tropical planning.

Methods

The two most important modifications required in methods concern the worker rather than the product—moderation of heavy and hot labor, and reduction of dependence upon human judgment or, at least, the creation of safeguards against faulty judgment. These aspects were discussed in Chapter 5 on human health and efficiency. For the material aspects, most attention should be given to those instances where temperature or humidity affect some quality of the item which is critical to its treatment or to its final state. Storage and preservation during transportation may well create major problems in a hot humid environment, but these do not differ essentially from the similar problems which have been discussed earlier in relation to food.

Power

Five years ago one would have been content to confine the discussion to a brief plea for the greater use of conventional fuels—timber, coal, petroleum products—supplemented where possible by water power, wind, or solar energy. One might have added, in the present connection, that the supplemental sources were all markedly dependent upon climatic conditions, and that a careful survey would have to be made in any given area to see whether shortage in fossil fuels warranted dependence to any extent upon the more erratic climatic sources of energy.

Today the bright new star of nuclear power is ascending the sky, and all long-range power questions must be examined in its light. Nuclear power is at present more costly than power from conventional sources when produced in the industrialized countries (20), but it may well be cheaper than conventional power in less developed regions. When the cost of antecedents to conventional power production (such as mines and dams) and the cost of concomitants (such as long transmission lines and continuing import of fuel) are added, the balance may be strongly tipped in favor of nuclear power in those areas. The present disadvantages of nuclear power —critical technology, relatively large units, high initial cost —will undoubtedly diminish with time. It is wise, therefore, to give careful thought to the new source when considering power developments in relatively undeveloped countries. It is almost paradoxical that this newest and most technical creation of technology seems to be the one most readily adaptable to both the needs and the circumstances of the nontechnological regions.

PREFERENTIAL REGIONS

The factors to be taken into account in deciding where best to promote industrial development are quite similar to those mentioned in connection with crop production, animal husbandry, and human welfare, except that here the climatic factors carry somewhat less weight. The primary considerations would logically be the existence of raw materials, labor, and potential markets; but political expediency may override this. The greatest returns for investment could be expected in a country where industrialization is already under way, but where technical and economic assistance is insufficient. As against this, however, protection and conservation of past investments at the one extreme, and of simple humanitarian appeal at the other, may influence the decision. Undoubtedly the political stability of the country and the degree of cooperation that might be expected of the inhabitants are most important factors. The physical environment affects the decision chiefly through questions of transportation involving the practicability of road, rail, river, and air services.

There can be no simple set of patterns on which to base decisions. Indeed, the considerations are likely to vary profoundly from one place to another, even within a small country.

Chapter 7

PROSPECT

WE STARTED with the observation that about thirty per cent of the world's population lives in the tropic zone, and that many of the countries lying within that zone are underdeveloped. We noted that the changing pattern of world politics has placed the United States in a position of particular responsibility with regard to the tropics, in that we must now deal directly with those countries and, in so doing, order our relationships in a way which will not only promote their immediate welfare, but also help to build a world in which the good life will be within reach of all.

While we are primarily concerned here with the role that the climatic regimes of the tropics may play in retarding economic development, the question cannot be answered in terms of science and scholarship alone. Statesmanship and foreign policy are also involved, since, in providing that science and scholarship, we are placed in the difficult position of giving leadership without dominance, advice without dictation, and assistance without control.

Four times has the basic question, "What effects may climate have upon attempts to increase productivity in the tropics?" been posed—in relation to each of the four fields of crop production, animal husbandry, human efficiency, and industry. The answers that have emerged have dealt not only with the basic question, but also with measures for improving the situation, nonclimatic factors which may interfere with that improvement, and even the matter of where limited effort may be best applied.

A certain uniformity was preserved in the way in which the answers were set out in the four major fields; but emphasis varied, and certain specific topics were discussed when it seemed opportune. The answers will now be reviewed, first to note the role played by climatic factors, second to appre-

ciate the influence of nonclimatic factors, third to see what
can be done in the light of existing knowledge, and finally
to determine what further research and development are
required to ensure success for our difficult task.

THE ROLE OF CLIMATE

Moderately high temperatures, high humidities, heavy
precipitation, frequent flooding, fairly intense sunlight
evenly distributed throughout the year, and sometimes high
wind, characterize the humid tropics. The different elements
affect the various aspects of man's activities in many different
ways, sometimes beneficially, but more often adversely.
These effects, good and bad, may be conveniently summarized in relation to each of our four major topics of plant
production, animal production, human efficiency, and industry.

In Plant Production

By hastening the decay of organic material, the high temperatures and humidities promote the turnover of the available nutritional capital, but they also expose it to depreciation by leaching and erosion. Heavy rain greatly increases
the tendency to washing out the nutrients and to wasteful
erosion. It often results in flood damage to crops as well; but
floods are useful to the extent that they deposit fertile silt on
lands otherwise depleted.

Plant growth and multiplication are, in general, greatly
favored by the high temperatures and humidities, especially
if the complex of ecologically interdependent forms is preserved. This complex, however, represents a delicate balance
in a basically precarious situation, and numerous actual or
potential disease agents and pests are included in the complex. Multiple plant species, each having different requirements, help to maintain the balance; pure stands militate
against it and open the way for widespread disease. Tropical
plants tend to have relatively low concentrations of minerals
and protein; food crops are apt to be of the carbohydrate
type.

The number of crops that can be grown in sufficient den-
sity and with sufficient yield for commercial exploitation

tends to be limited, but there is less climatic restriction upon small-scale production. Cultivation and harvesting, except by primitive methods, are made difficult by heavy rain, while storage is adversely affected by the prevailing temperatures and humidities.

In Animal Production

Although plentiful, forage is low in mineral and protein content, for the reasons just given. It tends to be high in fiber content which adds to the alimentary burden of the animal; and it is likely to be deficient in trace elements as well as in the major minerals. Small animals may have a survival advantage over larger ones of the same species.

Infectious disease and parasitism are particularly favored by the moderately high temperatures and high humidities. Free-living agents, vectors, and host reservoirs, form part of the tropical ecological complex.

While the climate is generally tolerable for unimproved, low-producing, indigenous animals whose demands do not go beyond the feeding capacity of the area, it may impose an important heat stress upon animals who are unadapted to the conditions or whose metabolism has been stepped up by high production or high feeding. Artificial selection for high production may result in an impasse unless it is accompanied by increased efficiency in food utilization. Heat stress may result in reduced production, decreased resistance to disease, or lowered fertility.

Climate affects management chiefly through the difficulty it creates in supplying sufficient nutriment for the animals and by the necessity it imposes for constantly combatting various types of infection. Animal products deteriorate rapidly in tropical climates unless preservation is vigorously practiced.

In Human Health and Efficiency

The direct physiological effects of climate which impair efficiency may occur in newcomers but tend to disappear with acclimatization. The actual capacity for work may be little changed, but a disinclination for work persists, although appropriate incentives may restore output. Apart from this, no permanent deleterious direct effects occur in healthy persons living under natural tropical conditions; but artificial conditions, as in hot industries or badly designed houses, may continue to exert effects.

Some reduction of mental initiative is probably the most important single direct result of tropical environments. Accuracy may be affected in poorly motivated persons, and the need for increased concentration may be felt as a strain. There is little evidence for attributing personality changes to climate as such.

As with plants and animals, the climatic conditions favor the occurrence and transmission of certain infectious diseases. Free-living organisms like cholera vibrios and the larvae of hookworms; vectors like flies, mosquitoes, and mites; and both human and animal reservoirs of disease are encouraged by the equable conditions. Heat stress may at times increase human susceptibility to infection.

Malnutrition may be facilitated by the reduced mineral and protein content of plant foods or by the relative scarcity of animal foods, but climate as such is a minor factor in the causation of the widespread malnutrition.

In Industry

The effects of climate on man, be he manager or laborer, have been discussed. Insofar as the material aspects of industry are concerned, heavy rainfall interferes with transportation by making bogs out of unpaved roads and airfields, and by producing floods; but it may help by creating and maintaining navigable rivers. High temperatures, high humidities, and fairly intense sunshine combine to promote deterioration in many materials and may interfere with some industrial processes. The high rainfall may permit the development of hydroelectric power where it is fairly well distributed over the year or where suitable sites can be found for dams. Although solar energy has some special applications, it does not offer a very practical source of additional industrial power.

THE ROLE OF NONCLIMATIC FACTORS

Numerous and important though the climatic influences are, nonclimatic factors exercise equal, if not greater, influences upon the economic situation in the tropics. It is desirable to enumerate those that have been briefly discussed in preceding chapters, if only because they interact so closely with the climatic factors and affect countermeasures. The list can hardly hope to be systematic or complete—important considerations have no doubt been overlooked, and some factors may appear under more than one heading—but it will serve to put the climatic influences in some perspective. Nonclimatic factors vary greatly in nature and intensity from place to place and are undergoing rapid change in many countries. Nothing more than generalizations are possible here, but the reader who is interested in a particular area would do well to examine carefully the extent to which any one of them applies there.

Land Tenure

Lack of ownership may not in itself greatly upset the peasant. But when it is accompanied by insecurity, insufficient sharing in the produce of the land, or perpetual economic subservience to the owner, it must inevitably interfere with effective and wise utilization. Sequestration of land for nonproductive purposes, or uneconomic use of land, detracts from the national productivity. Multiple subdivision, especially if it results in the separation of plots belonging to the same owner, makes care and harvesting difficult. Although not confined to the tropics, these and other unsatisfactory features of land use have been sufficiently widespread in those regions to constitute a severe restriction upon agricultural development. In many regions, however, improvements are being effected.

Methods

The widespread practice of shifting cultivation is consistent with a subsistence economy as long as the practice is strictly controlled and employed only where there is a large proportion of land to population. It is progressively destructive, however, when used frequently or extensively, and is quite incompatible with economic development beyond the primitive subsistence level. Widespread deforestation, often undertaken as a first step to commercial crop production, is even more destructive and detrimental to a permanent economy. With few exceptions, successful and continuing crop production requires that a compromise be worked out between the conditions required for crops on the one hand, and the maintenance of soil fertility and quality on the other. Good results can be expected from fertilizers only when they are introduced into a fairly stable earth-crop cycle of nutrients, and when they are adjusted to conform to the real needs of the local situation. Many primitive methods of tilling, planting, and harvesting are well adapted and should not be radically disturbed unless the circumstances themselves are markedly altered. Opportunities for mechanization are restricted by the subdivision of holdings, mixed planting, and broken land, as much as by ignorance and poverty. Even where it is possible to introduce mechanization, major modifications may be necessary in the machines and the uses to which they are put.

In most tropical countries, only a small proportion of the population has any acquaintance with more than simple mechanical methods, and a still smaller proportion can boast of any mechanical skill. While such people may learn to use automobiles and other machines in an empirical fashion, they do not readily appreciate the importance of maintenance or acquire the technical outlook necessary to really efficient operation. A fairly considerable time must be allowed for reorientation before much success can be expected from introduced technology, even where other circumstances indicate its usefulness.

Social Restraints

The triad of conservatism, ignorance, and poverty has been mentioned frequently in the preceding chapters. Too poor to learn, too ignorant to improve, and too frightened to try, a large mass of the tropical peasantry is seemingly doomed to an endless round of inadequacy. Here and there a spark may be kindled, now and then an improvement made; but, in spite of a growing awareness of the outside world, such people may still present a considerable drag to any progressive force.

Somewhat allied to these restraints, but operating at a different level, are the sanctions of the social code. Fashioned as protective regulations, but now outmoded, various proscriptions impede the full realization of possible improvements. Some concern technical methods, others the dignity of labor, and many more the consumption of foods. Until some way is found of tempering them to present-day realities, such taboos limit the progress of economic development.

For certain groups, isolation is a thing to be cherished, and economic development something to be avoided or at least indefinitely postponed. While this attitude must be respected, and while the main course of tropical develop ment may temporarily pass such groups by, it seems inevitable that "progress" will eventually overtake them. Cognizance must be taken of them, not merely because they represent a present inertia, but because their integration will create problems in the future.

Economic Status

With too little capital to undertake development, and too little development to create capital, many areas are doomed to remain at their present poor level, entirely apart from any advantages or disadvantages of climate, unless positive assistance is obtained. Whether or not such assistance can be expected depends upon at least three nonclimatic circumstances—the extent of natural resources, the availability of labor, and the amenability of the people.

An increasing number of natural resources are being found in the tropics, but developing them and marketing the products present great problems. Not so long ago the tropics were fervently believed to be a rich source of cheap labor; but a drastic revaluation of the labor position has been necessary. In certain areas there is an absolute shortage of labor; in others, inhabitants are unwilling to accept the new idea of work. And even where there is an abundance of labor certain limitations have become quite clear. The requirement for unskilled labor diminishes as technology advances; its reliability decreases as supervision becomes remote. Industry frequently finds itself placed awkwardly between two worlds when it tries to operate in the tropics— it has relatively little use for the abundant unskilled labor of the more primitive world, and it suffers from an acute shortage of the technical and supervisory personnel necessary to the technological world. Time will undoubtedly provide a solution, but for the present there is bound to be many a disturbing hiatus.

The disinclination of individuals for work is a minor problem, compared with those created by political instability, which at the present time may well constitute one of the major difficulties confronting tropical development. History may later reveal that current disturbances are but the growing pains of new-found freedom and nationalism; but they certainly create misgivings while they last. In politically troubled areas, there is little point in considering the more delicate and refined problems of possible climatic influence until much greater calm, stability and the assurance of continued effort prevail.

THE APPLICATION OF PRESENT KNOWLEDGE

From the foregoing summaries it is quite clear that certain difficulties, some of climatic but more of nonclimatic origin, attend the development of tropical countries. Previous chapters have also revealed with equal clarity that a considerable body of knowledge exists, which, if properly applied, would go a long way toward meeting those difficulties. Largely using the sequence of headings employed in previous chapters, the outline that follows indicates the main fields where existing knowledge could be better applied. The relative importance of the various measures listed, the details to be considered, and the feasibility of putting them into operation, will vary greatly from place to place. A close study of the prevailing situation and a careful judgment of what would be the most profitable course of action are essential in any particular locality. In every instance the question of cost in relation to expected return will call for serious consideration. Categorical answers cannot be given in the face of so many variables, but the following items should receive careful scrutiny.

In Plant Production

Ecology—Appreciation of the interrelatedness of living things, and the danger of thinking of single types apart from all the circumstances in which they must live; and in particular the risk incurred by pure stands.

Conservation—The overwhelming importance of preserving the slender nutrient capital against the rapid depreciating effects of leaching and erosion; the disadvantages of many common practices, both native and technological; and possible methods of restricting losses.

Selection—The relative advantages and disadvantages of different species or types under various environmental circumstances; and methods of selecting preferred strains.

Planting—Adaptation of methods and systems to promote conservation, obtain mutual advantages for coexistent plants, facilitate care, and assist harvesting.

Fertilizing—The importance of using natural fertilizing by silt, green manure, and animal manure; necessity for choosing chemical fertilizer in relation to soil and plant needs; need for closing the soil-plant cycle of nutrients to conserve fertilizer.

Disease control—Susceptibility of pure stands; distribution of resistance between strains; methods and limitations of chemical control.

Crop care—Methods and dangers of weed control; uses and abuses of irrigation; protection from storm and flood damage.

Harvesting—Improvements on primitive methods; uses and limitations of mechanical methods; methods for securing successional maturation.

Storage and transportation—Protection from rain, humidity, vermin, and mold; drying; preservation; canning; freezing.

Marketing—Extending its scope; meeting consumer requirements; lessening seasonal fluctuations in supply.

In Animal Production

Ecology—Economic as well as biological role of animals in existing and possible future complexes.

Selection and breeding—Recognition of desirable qualities for particular circumstances; methods of selection; principles of improvement by breeding.

Nutrition—Recognition of animal requirements; importance of efficiency in food utilization; necessity for pasture control; role of mineral deficiencies.

Care and management—Control of disease; protection from environmental stress.

Collection of product—Importance of carefulness; place of grading and quality control; improvements on simple methods; uses and limitations of mechanical methods.

Storage and transportation—Prevention of deterioration; hygienic aspects; preservation; canning; cold storage.

Marketing—As for plant products.

In Human Welfare

Disease control—Elimination of vectors; screening of persons; suppressive medication; immunization; general hygiene.

Nutrition—Importance of nutrients; conservation of nutrients; increased variety of foods; substitution for shortages.

Working conditions—Improvement of hygienic conditions; nature of occupational disease; control of atmospheric conditions; basic concepts of "human engineering."

Housing and clothing—Improvement of hygienic conditions; adaption to climatic conditions.

Incentives—Overwhelming importance of desire for improvement; nature of factors weakening incentive; positive measures for increasing incentive; the dignity of labor.

In Industry

Prevention of deterioration—Nature of deterioration; preventive methods; relative cost of measures; selection of materials.

Modification of methods—Recognized modifications; need for ingenuity.

Transportation—Need for broad survey; selection of routes; stabilization of soils; modification of vehicles.

Power—Need for realistic evaluation of sources; problems of storage and transmission.

Labor—Limitations of unskilled labor; need for technical and supervisory personnel; problems of relocation; importance of incentives.

Capital—Sources of supply; importance of political stability and security.

Setting

Confronted by such an extensive list of items in which remedial action is possible right now, and realizing that each subject in the list embraces a large number of allied items, one is apt to be filled with a sense of urgency and an impatience with the apparent slowness of progress. To a certain extent this is a legitimate and desirable reaction. Current progress is slow; more could undoubtedly be done. But haste is not the best adviser. The problem is not the comparatively simple one with which we are familiar in technological communities of getting more money, building more facilities, hiring more instructors—not that these are easy, even in our community. The problems are much more complex, solutions much less definite. The cultural setting is apt to be vastly different from that to which we are accustomed, with a different set of values, different objectives, and different antecedents. The key to successful education is creating a desire for it in those who are to receive it. Unless the recipients are convinced that the instruction is something that they need and that the result will be enlightenment in a very realistic sense, much of the labor will be in vain. To paraphrase a recent review, what is educationally desirable may be socially unacceptable, what is socially desirable may be economically unattractive, or what is economically attractive may be politically impracticable.[1]

People who have enjoyed, after a fashion, a long period

[1] Review of *Education and Social Change in Tropical Areas* by M. Read (London: Thomas Nelson & Sons, 1955), published in *Nature*, v. 176 (1955), p. 757.

of equilibrium, albeit at a low level, will not automatically accept the proposition that they should bestir themselves and strive for a new state of affairs, even though we assure them it is a superior one. They are especially likely to be skeptical when we reveal the instabilities, neuroses, frustrations, and fears that stalk our modern world. Men are apt to change a stable way of life only in response to the pressure of severe competition from without, or to the repeated suggestion that prestige will be gained. The reality and immediacy of the former may be very apparent to us; but the forces of tradition, abetted by vested interests in continuity, tend to hide it from the inhabitants—sometimes very successfully.

This dilution of significance is one of the first things that the apostle of technology must take into consideration. Thus chastened, he may underestimate the alternative power— that of repeated suggestion. But this is often effective, although sometimes in an odd and misplaced fashion. Educational practice must face the realities of the local situation and adapt its method to those realities without losing faith in the fundamental worth of what it has to offer. Above all, it must demonstrate the practicality of its teaching, the obvious advantage to the individual of the knowledge gained.

Methods

To be successful, educational effort must be applied widely, systematically, and continuously. Sporadic effort is largely wasted effort. Higher education is ineffective unless there is a broad base of popular understanding upon which it can work. Objectives will be missed unless the instruction given at different levels is integrated. We, in the technological countries, are so accustomed to taking a certain basic education for granted that we are apt to overlook the importance of basic instruction in many less-developed regions. The multiplicity of levels at which instruction may be necessary if development is to succeed, and some of the objectives appropriate to each, may be presented in outline form:

"*Grass roots*"—Winning the farmer's, worker's, and householder's confidence; demonstrating the significance for the individual; improvement of traditional methods as a first step; dignity of labor.

Regional service—Provision of routine technical help for improvement of farming, industry, health on individual or group basis; introduction of basic concepts of science and technology; collection of information on problems, suitability of proposals, need for adjustments; extension service.

School system—Encouragement of desire for improvement; explanation of fuller life; introduction to basic concepts of science and technology; participation in agricultural, domestic, or industrial projects.

Adult education—Explanation of immediate and ultimate benefits; encouragement of community effort; promotion of family participation.

Technical training—Training for supervision, technical responsibility, organization.

Specialist training—Training of highly selected personnel in systematic disciplines leading to responsible specialization and research.

While it may be necessary to bring a few highly selected persons to the technological countries for specialist training, most training should be provided in the native countries, where it can be kept in touch with realities and its operation can be appreciated by the population at large. Experts from technological countries should be made available to the extent that they are required, especially in the earlier stages of the educational program. But it is highly desirable that the various countries seek to assume responsibility for their own technical and developmental welfare as soon as possible, joining on an equal footing with other countries in the normal free interchange of technical and scientific experience.

RESEARCH AND DEVELOPMENT

Undoubtedly a thorough application of existing knowledge would bring about a marked improvement in the economic and general welfare of tropical countries, and this application should certainly be pressed with all the power at our command. But this is only the beginning of what is required of us. Technological countries take great pride in the tradition of research which has brought them to their present state of practical ability. Yet, in the pursuit of the immediate benefits to be gained from this ability, they are apt to lose sight of the necessity for supporting more research from which still further advances in technology can be expected in the future. The activities of organizations devoted to assisting underdeveloped countries, be the organizations international, national, or industrial, are very largely taken up with the exploitation and application of existing knowledge. Such organizations are usually permitted or willing to make only a small proportion of their resources available for research, unless that research is closely tied to specific problems with a fairly high chance of providing answers in the fairly immediate future. There are, of course, exceptions, but the opportunities presented by those exceptions are far too few for equanimity.

Setting

To a certain extent tropical interests can expect to depend upon the research which goes on in the more technological centers, and there is every reason to take the fullest advantage of what is already in progress. But excessive dependence is undesirable from many points of view. Whatever purists may say, much of the basic stimulus to research and a very large part of the material support for research come from the need to meet practical problems. If this research is concentrated in or dependent upon temperate countries, the problems of those countries will naturally be first served, and tropical problems will correspondingly tend to be overlooked. True, research frequently comes up with explanations and ideas far removed from the problem for which it was initiated, but the chances of this kind of happy accident are too slim to provide much comfort for those faced with tropical problems. There is a clear need for the conduct of research with a tropical orientation in addition to that pursued in nontropical countries. However, great difficulties, mainly of a cultural nature, at once arise.

The motivation, methodology, and staffing of present-day

research have developed from and are largely predicated on technological development; great difficulties must be expected if one proposes to set up similar activities in a widely different set of environmental and cultural circumstances. In the early years of this century colonial interests were sufficiently strong for several European powers to support research in tropical areas, especially in the field of tropical medicine; and a number of excellent men were stimulated to spend many years, often under the most difficult circumstances, in its pursuit. This driving force has now dwindled, and in the meantime research has become much more complicated. There is an increasing reluctance on the part of scientists, young and old alike, to leave the exciting and rewarding opportunities in their own countries for the nebulous, difficult, and uncomfortable conditions of less-developed countries. If, here and there, a scientist is sufficiently inspired to go, the chances are that his wife will object. The magic of the phrase "outpost of empire" has been lost; we have nothing to put in its place.

Rapid advances in tropical research cannot be expected until the tropical peoples themselves accept the responsibility, provide the means, and acquire the competent personnel. In this, as in so many aspects of development, tropical countries are faced with the prospect of compressing into a few years the changes of thought and habit that we have acquired over centuries, and this is probably more difficult to achieve in research than in any other aspect. The questioning, critical, and precise habit of thought which is essential to good research is not easily acquired, even in our own country where such attitudes are encouraged in the population at large. Its development is so much more difficult in a culture where acceptance, repetition, and symbolism have ruled the thought processes for centuries. The outward forms may be easily acquired, but the inner understanding comes slowly; and outward form without inner substance is dangerous.

The transitional period in which we are today is difficult and frustrating. We must still try to encourage scientists from the temperate zones to work in tropical countries, while simultaneously urging tropical countries to set up their own organizations. Of neither, however, can we expect more than moderate compliance. It is difficult to get good men to go permanently to the tropics: the older ones are already established here, the younger see too many opportunities at home. Underdeveloped countries, on the other hand, need their best men for immediate development; and those who do come to temperate countries for research training often develop an unwillingness to return. We must accept the fact that this is a period of transition, congratulate ourselves on the successes that have been achieved (and there are several notable instances), and press ahead on both fronts in the faith that adjustment will improve as the research outlook becomes absorbed into the tropical cultures.

Topics

In designating fields in which research is needed one can do no more than indicate the general directions that appear fruitful. Each field may be divided in an infinite number of ways, and the worker must be left free to choose the particular segment that appeals to him and is important to his country. The following list will suffice to indicate the broad scope of the problems visible at this time. The future may well add new and even more important topics.

Climate—Fundamental determinants; distribution of elements in time and space; techniques for informative representation.

Soils—Life history and rational classification; distribution; chemical and physical properties; stabilization and restitution; microbiology; soil-plant relationships.

Plants and animals—Mechanisms of climatic effects; genetic potentialities; breeding for productivity and resistance; ecology; disease production and control; nutrition; realization of potentialities by management; handling and marketing of products.

Man—Mechanisms of climatic effect; long-term adaptation; disease prevention and control; psychological responses to physical and social environment; social integration; factors affecting adaptation; genetic variation; housing and clothing; racial adaptability.

Industry—Opportunities and needs; adaptation of methods;

selection and preservation of materials; cost control; human engineering; automation; power development; capital formation; motivation.

In this list, as indeed throughout this section, no distinction has been made between research and development. There is no sharp dividing line, and little agreement can be obtained on where to attempt one; but care must be taken that the research program is not driven across the indeterminate boundary by the constant and natural pressure to deal with the here and now, rather than with the uncertain future.

Synthesis

At this point it is appropriate to deal with one aspect of research which does not fit into the list given above—for the very good reason that it embraces all the topics mentioned. As knowledge increases and the techniques of further research become more complex, the scope that can be covered by any one person progressively narrows. Logical method, moreover, lends itself to subdividing the field of discourse, but offers much less assistance to the converse process of integrating the information obtained in various segments so that broad questions can be answered. Very seldom does a practical problem lend itself to solution in one narrow field of knowledge. On the contrary, it must usually be broken down into component parts which can be examined by different groups, each skilled in some special field. Research organizations and academic institutions alike follow this procedure; but there is little formal provision for putting the sectional answers together to constitute a solution of the original problem. This exceedingly important process is too often conducted in a haphazard or even arbitrary fashion. A practice which has most to commend it, is for representatives of the various study groups to meet and come to a majority decision; but even here the basis for taking the decision is often obscure. Cost, expediency, personality, precedent, or plain wishful thinking may determine the weight given to the various pieces of evidence and the nature of the final decision. More usually, the specialist reports are reviewed by some one person who, not having the necessary insight into the various aspects for evaluating their several contributions, selects some and discards others out of proportion to their true significance. Matters may be made even worse if the specialist considerations are summarized, interpreted, and extracted en route, as so very commonly occurs.

This problem of integrating specialist reports in order to answer broad problems badly needs study; it is one that has special relevance to the problem of economic development of the tropics. In a limited and modest way the present report is an example of one approach. Specialists concerned with the more obvious aspects are assembled in conference, and the problem is put to them. After analyzing their segments, they report back to a full conference at which their contributions are examined, further questions asked, and a preliminary synthesis attempted. The specialists make further studies; more specialists are consulted; more combined meetings are held—but always under the watchful insistence of a secretariat which preserves the main question and continuously seeks the means of integrating the answers with each other. Finally, when sufficient information seems to be available, the secretariat (or, more usually, one member of it) prepares a draft report indicating the several analyses and suggesting the integrated answer. This is then subjected to careful scrutiny by the participants, amended where necessary, and finally adopted as the most acceptable solution.

This procedure, which is simply an extension of the round-table method, will work with some problems, but it is rather demanding on the personnel—participants must be prepared to work integratively, the secretariat must have wide vision and comprehension, and the chairmanship must be sound. Moreover, it is not a rapid process. It may remain the method of choice for broad or important policy decisions, but it needs to be supplemented by more rapid, less demanding, and better defined methods for less weighty decisions. The outlook and methods developed by those who practice "operations research" offer some promise, although at present they tend to deal with limited and easily quantifiable processes. Certainly, modern computers should be put to work where the information lends itself to treatment. Idealistic though the concepts and solutions would be, they would constitute patterns upon which modifications could be made as necessary to meet the variables and intangibles of realistic situations.

Facilities

Probably the ideal method of promoting research is to find the man who is interested in doing it, who has in fact already obtained promising results, and to give him what he needs to be fully effective. In a well-developed community, where schools, colleges, and universities provide the basic training and almost any bright man can get enough support to test his skill, this might well be adopted as the central policy. But it hardly seems sufficient under the kind of circumstances that we have been considering. At least for the transitional period until tropical countries are in the position to order their own developmental problems without assistance, the great need is to have stable nuclei around which research can crystallize and from which other centers can be born as opportunity offers. In other words, and to use the formal name, research institutes are needed.

For reasons already given in this chapter, these research institutes should be located in the tropics, but should retain close contact with, and receive more than moral support from, the research centers of temperate lands. Easy enough to enunciate, this principle has not always met with success in execution. The difficulties as well as the desirability should be examined, and the necessary conditions for success established.

The great advantage of a research institute is that it provides continuity and some measure of security in a changeable world. If wisely constituted, it will have guaranteed funds with which to provide the basic accommodation, equipment, and services required by most research programs, so that individual projects would not have to deplete their financial grants with such nonspecialist provisions. By its permanence, the institute would symbolize the essential continuity of effort, even though problems and projects change, and attract the potential worker, perhaps long before he has acquired the skills necessary to his own effort. A walk past a famous institute, or even a picture postcard, has fired the imagination of many a young man and secured a recruit to the life of research. From a gathering together of men with various skills, different outlooks, and dissimilar objectives, come new ideas, critical consideration, and breadth of outlook—the very pabulum of productive research. From their work springs repute, and from the repute fresh recruits, further assistance, and permanent standards.

Or so one would hope! In point of fact this happy progress is not always realized. Too many institutes, admittedly outside of the tropics as well as in, have started in a wave of optimism and confidence, only to fail or, worse still, to languish and suffer derogatory comment. Much more than optimism and good intentions are required. A sufficient income must certainly be guaranteed if the institute is to flourish and not dissipate its energy in endeavors which are starved for want of the essentials. Lack of financial support has undoubtedly caused the failure of some and severely limited the success of other institutions; but even adequate finance is not enough. Any organization which is set up away from the main cultural centers must experience difficulty in obtaining and maintaining a first-rate staff. It may be forced to approach a highly competitive market with too little to offer, not necessarily in a financial sense, but in terms of those intangibles which serve as fringe benefits for scientific personnel—contact with their own kind, position in the main stream of scientific endeavor, many pupils. Here and there an institute has had the unusual good luck to find one of the exceptions, a thoroughly competent man who is completely wrapped up in the tropical problem and who has managed to have his family share his content, perhaps a man who is so outstanding that the stream of science actually seeks him. Such a person could very well solve the whole problem of institutional integrity if he also happened to have the personality which creates scientific comradeship. But such men are glorious exceptions, the true pioneers who create progress wherever they are. To them must go a large share of the credit, but even their influence is limited. They are usually specialists, and unless they are supported by other, though lesser, efforts to promote the steady growth of well-directed scientific inquiry, the community as a whole will not derive full benefit.

Between the well-established universities, schools, and research centers of the technological countries on the one hand, and the steadily growing number of scholastic institutions in tropical countries on the other, there is a commendable co-operation as evidenced by agreements for exchange of staff and students, organization of research expeditions with joint participation, and attendance at international meetings. These cooperative activities are financed by both private foundations and governmental expenditure on a moderately generous scale and should in time serve greatly to promote tropical development.

The question arises, nevertheless, as to whether more might not be done to focus these influences upon the whole matter of tropical development, rather than to leave their influence to chance. Research cannot and should not be directed, in the sense that individuals are told what to study and how to orient their activities to the welfare of the state. Yet it seems only reasonable that the results of these individual activities should be examined for their relevance to national problems and applied in co-ordinated fashion to that end where suitable. Tentative and uncertain though the procedures of synthesis may be, they would accelerate a resolution of the complex problems of development if applied to the ideas and evidence emerging from specialized studies by individual scholars and institutions.

The super-university, or super-research-institution, may be an answer, but from what has been said above, this seems doubtful. There would appear to be some promise, however, for an organization which would not merely act as a clearing house for information between all the institutions and agencies concerned, but attempt to synthesize the information into a coherent body of knowledge on tropical development and assist individual countries to apply that knowledge to specific situations. If located in a technological country, such an organization would have the advantage of drawing upon a wide range of talents and experienced men and should have little trouble in securing first-class staff. Considerable travel would be necessary for its interpretive staff; and many of its

envoys, perhaps on loan from other institutions, would need
to conduct on-the-spot studies of local conditions if general
principles are to be applied to specific situations.

CONCLUSION

The problem of tropical development should be pursued
with all speed and all possible support, but on a broad front
in which the climate, man, agriculture, industry, and economics receive simultaneous consideration. I believe that the
problem is sufficiently important and urgent, and that the
prospect of significant improvement is sufficiently clear, to
warrant the generous financial support of a long-term, intensive, comprehensive study set up on a nonofficial basis.

This personal conviction found strong support at the conference which concluded the work of the Council on Foreign
Relations' Study Group. A small committee under the chairmanship of Stacy May set out in summary form its estimate
of the results of the survey some excerpts from which may
serve as a fitting conclusion to this report.

1. We are convinced that the United States has an important
interest in far more general and more dynamic economic, social,
and political progress in the underdeveloped areas of the free
world than has been achieved to date.

We believe that the achievement of such progress would be of
basic importance to the United States' economy, its security, and
its international relations, even if the world political crisis that
faces us today had never developed in its present form.

2. In the deliberations of this group it has been noted that
among the nations of the free world there is a striking coincidence between the factor of tropicality and the lack of progress,
as measured by a variety of indexes, that is denominated a state
of underdevelopment.

We have reviewed evidence that convincingly demonstrates
that tropicality is not the exclusive crucial factor in underdevelopment, since there are certain nations with tropical environments that have achieved at least a relatively high degree of
advancement and there are others that are clearly to be classified
as underdeveloped which are well within the temperate zones.

However, both the degree of coincidence, and a variety of

conclusive evidence that clearly indicates that most peoples within the tropical areas suffer a variety of disadvantageous handicaps as compared with temperate-zone dwellers, have convinced us that there are special difficulties directly or indirectly affecting human habitation of tropical environments, particularly the humid tropics.

Far more, and more searching, research than has been carried out to date is needed to separate folklore and inference from certainly established fact. It is particularly important to obtain clearer guidelines than presently exist in order to define the incidence, characteristics, and degree of tropical conditions that impose a prohibitively heavy burden upon successful human adaptation; to determine how far less extreme tropical environments impose burdens which, though real, are indirect rather than direct in their effect upon inhabitants; to discover how many of either the direct or indirect unfavorable influences are remediable; and to ascertain whether known remedies are applicable within cost limits that are practically supportable in a competitive world. There is even need for far more complete and particularized climatological information on tropical countries, in form and detail that will allow adequate analysis of the effect of these conditions on agricultural, pastoral, industrial and social development. We believe that the deficiencies in these and other relevant fields should be speedily made good.

3. Because of our conviction of the importance of this field to United States interests, we believe that intensive research should be pursued to the end that our knowledge about the limiting influence of tropical environment upon human progress may be better understood, and the means of applying remedies where and to the degree practicable may be determined.

Our initial examination of the field has revealed a considerable number of avenues of research that we believe to be subject to investigation by known methods, and that we are confident will yield promising results if pursued with sufficient intensity, for a sufficiently sustained period, under the most appropriate auspices.

4. Because the complex of relevant factors that we have examined and that are set forth in our proceedings is so intricate, we believe that sound progress is dependent upon enlisting the sustained research effort of competent scholars from a consider-

able variety of academic disciplines, some but not all of which
have been represented in our meetings. Detailed assembly of
basic information not presently available in usable form or adequate amount must be prepared by representatives of each discipline and subjected to careful testing and analysis. We feel
sure that the problem calls for a high degree of synthesis as well
as specialized investigation and that this can only be supplied
through interdisciplinary teamwork that is continuous throughout the planning, experimental, collating and analytical stages.

We feel sure that the cooperative effort must embrace both laboratory investigation in advanced centers of research and scholarship, such as are found in temperate countries, and sustained
investigation in tropical areas with the collaboration of indigenous scholars; that this investigation must be conducted in a
considerable variety of tropical centers to assure that proper
allowance is made for the wide variations of climatological, cultural, political, economic, and social factors that are known to
exist. We should recommend also that the investigations should
include a sufficient representation of the cultural studies to take
account of factors which are intimately related to development.
This is dictated by the logic that impels us to study tropic climate *because* of its relevance to development progress.

5. We have arrived at the further conviction that effective work
in this field calls for an approach that is long-term. No swift
results that are likely to stand up as authoritative are to be expected, and it is requisite that the program be organized under
auspices and with support that will assure the necessary scope
and continuity. Generalizations are to be sought only to the
extent that they have usable validity; the variations of climate,
resources, population densities, peoples, and cultures between
areas are likely, in our judgment, to make the findings that re-
late to particular situations far more susceptible to practical
application.

6. We believe that the project is sufficiently broad and demanding to require all the support that it can be expected to
command. It might be organized under the auspices and with
financial backing of national governments, international agencies, or private foundations, and might well receive the contributions of private businesses. Almost certainly, its operations
would be most effectively carried out by university or research

centers that embraced the considerable variety of personnel representing the several disciplines required. The same would apply to the operations in tropical field investigations.

There are advantages and disadvantages in each of the several sponsoring and supporting agencies proposed. There is probably room for all, but care should be taken to organize the several projects, into which the complete enterprise might well break down, under a sponsorship that will be acceptable to the area with which the operation directly deals.

7. It is important that the focus of the project should be upon the broad problem of the influence of tropical climates upon indigenous populations and the development progress, rather than just on temperate zone sojourners in the tropics.

We should impute a similar importance to the need for re-thinking the whole problem in terms that are meaningful to tropical peoples, without taking it for granted that either the aspirations or the procedures of the temperate zones are directly transferable.

8. We believe that there is need to place considerable emphasis on educating the public to the importance of this problem, and that such effort should be exerted at home and abroad. It is important to educate the general public, officials and scholars everywhere, but the actual transfer of techniques to tropical areas should provide for education, at grass-roots level, of the people upon whom the use of the techniques in question actually depends.

SELECTED BIBLIOGRAPHY

The following items are referred to in the text, or were consulted for background information.

1a. Association for Applied Solar Energy. *Proceedings of the World Symposium on Applied Solar Energy.* Menlo Park, California: Stanford Research Institute, 1956. 300 p.

b. —————. *International Symposium on Applied Solar Energy.* 1955. Personal Notes.

2. Bates, M. *Where Winter Never Comes.* New York: Scribner, 1952. 309 p.

3. Bear, F. E. *Soils and Fertilizers.* New York: Wiley, 1954. 420 p.

4. Bingham, J. B. *Shirt-Sleeve Diplomacy: Point 4 in Action.* New York: Day, 1954. 303 p.

5. Brooks, C. E. P. *Climate in Everyday Life.* New York: Philosophical Library, 1951. 314 p.

6. Canada. Department of Mines and Technical Services. Geographical Branch. *Indo-China: A Geographical Appreciation.* Ottawa: Author, 1953. 88 p. (Foreign Geography Information Series, 6.)

7. Cilento, R. W. *The White Man in the Tropics.* Melbourne: Government Printer, 1925. 168 p. (Department of Health Service Publication, 7.)

8. Clark, C. *The Conditions of Economic Progress.* London: Macmillan, 2d ed., 1951, 567 p.

9. Dairy Herd Improvement Associations. *Letter,* v. 28, n. 8 (1952). 15 p.

10. Daniels, F. and Duffie, J. A. *Solar Energy Research.* Madison: University of Wisconsin Press, 1955. 290 p.

11. Dike, K. O. *Trade and Politics in the Niger Delta, 1830-1855.* New York: Oxford University Press, 1956. 250 p.

12. Dobzhansky, T. "Evolution in the Tropics," *American Scientist,* v. 38 (1950), pp. 209-21.

13a. Food and Agriculture Organization. *Dairy Products.* Rome: Author, 1953. 69 p. (FAO Commodity Series— Bulletin 24.)

b. ——————. *Report of the Second Inter-American Meeting on Livestock Production,* by R. W. Phillips. Rome: Author, 1953. 138 p. (FAO Development Paper, 33.)

c. ——————. *Report of the Third FAO Meeting on Livestock Production in the Americas.* Meeting Report No. 1955/11. Rome: Author, 1955. 170 p.

d. ——————. *The State of Food and Agriculture.* Rome: Author. Annual.

e. ——————. *Yearbook of Food and Agricultural Statistics.* Rome: Author. Annual.

14. Gourou, P. *The Tropical World: Its Social and Economic Conditions and Its Future Status.* London: Longmans, 1953. 152 p.

15a. Great Britain. Colonial Advisory Council of Agriculture. *Improvement of Cattle in British Colonial Territories in Africa.* London: HMSO, 1953. 144 p.

b. ——————. *Report of a Survey of Problems of Mechanization of Native Agriculture in Tropical African Colonies.* London: HMSO, 1954.

16. Greathouse, G. A. and Wessel, C. J. *Deterioration of Materials: Causes and Preventive Techniques.* New York: Reinhold, 1954. 835 p.

17a. Hanson, E. P. *New Worlds Emerging.* New York: Duell, 1949. 385 p.

b. ——————. *Transformation: The Story of Modern Puerto Rico.* New York: Simon & Schuster, 1955. 416 p.

18. Huntington, E. *Civilization and Climate.* New Haven: Yale University Press, 3d ed., 1924. 453 p.

19. India. Ministry of Information and Broadcasting. Publications Division. *First Five Year Plan.* Delhi: Author, 1953. 263 p.

20. International Conference on the Peaceful Uses of Atomic Energy, August 8-20, 1955. *Proceedings.* New York: International Documents Service, 1956. 16 v.

21. James, P. E. and Jones, C. F. *American Geography: Inventory and Prospect*. Syracuse: Syracuse University Press, 1954. 590 p.

22a. Kartha, K. P. R. *Milk Records of Cattle in Approved Dairy Farms in India*. New Delhi: Government of India Press, 1938. 175 p. (Imperial Council of Agricultural Research. Miscellaneous Bulletin, 18.)

  b. ————————. ————————. New Delhi: Government of India Press, 1941. 324 p. (Imperial Council of Agricultural Research. Miscellaneous Bulletin, 36, v. 1.)

23. Köppen, W. and Geiger, R. *Handbuch der Klimatologie*. Berlin: Borntraeger, 1936, v. 1, pt. C.

24a. Lee, D. H. K. *Manual of Field Studies on the Heat Tolerance of Domestic Animals*. Rome: Food and Agriculture Organization, 1954. 161 p. (FAO Development Paper, 38.)

  b. ————————. "Physiology as a Guide to Combatting Tropical Stress," *New England Journal of Medicine*, v. 243 (1950), pp. 723-30.

  c. ————————. *Physiological Objectives in Hot Weather Housing*. Washington: GPO, 1953. 79 p.

  d. ————————. *The Human Organism and Hot Environments*. Monograph prepared for Office of the Surgeon General, Department of Army. (In press.)

25. Lee, D. H. K. and Phillips, R. W. "Assessment of the Adaptability of Livestock to Climatic Stress," *Journal of Animal Science*, v. 7 (1948), pp. 391-425.

26. Mackworth, N. H. *Researches on the Measurement of Human Performance*. London: HMSO, 1950. 156 p. (Medical Research Council Special Report Series, 268.)

27. Markham, S. F. *Climate and the Energy of Nations*. Oxford: Oxford University Press, 1947. 240 p.

28. May, J. *Atlas of Disease*. A series of maps published by the American Geographical Society. For specific references see *Geographical Review*, 1950, v. 40 to date.

29. Mead, M., ed. *Cultural Patterns and Technical Change*. New York: Columbia University Press, 1953. 348 p.

30. Mills, C. A. *Climate Makes the Man*. New York: Harper, 1942. 320 p.

31.   Mitchell, H. H. and Edman, M. *Nutrition and Climatic Stress, with Particular Reference to Man.* Springfield: Charles C. Thomas, 1951. 234 p.

32.   Newburgh, L. H., ed. *Physiology of Heat Regulation and the Science of Clothing.* Philadelphia: Saunders, 1949. 457 p.

33.   O'Brien, J. P. "A Study of Miliaria Rubra, Tropical Anhidrosis and Anhidrotic Asthenia," *British Journal of Dermatology and Syphilology,* v. 59 (1947), pp. 125-58.

34.   Pendleton, R. L. "The Place of Tropical Soils in Feeding the World," *Ceiba,* v. 4 (1954), pp. 201-22.

35.   Phillips, R. W. "Animal Husbandry in China and India," *Journal of Animal Science,* v. 6 (1947), pp. 203-10.

       (*See also* Food and Agriculture Organization; Lee, D. H. K. and Phillips, R. W.)

36.   Precht, H., Christophersen, J. and Hensel, H. *Temperatur und Leben.* Berlin: Springer, 1955. 514 p.

37a.   Price, A. G. *White Settlers and Native Peoples.* London: Cambridge University Press, 1950. 232 p.

   b. —————. *White Settlers in the Tropics.* New York: American Geographical Society, 1939. 311 p.

38.   Putnam, P. *Energy in the Future.* New York: Van Nostrand, 1953. 556 p.

39.   Rhoad, A. O., ed. *Breeding Beef Cattle for Unfavorable Environments.* Austin: University of Texas Press, 1955. 248 p.

40.   Richards, P. W. *The Tropical Rain Forest; an Ecological Study.* London: Cambridge University Press, 1952. 450 p.

41.   Schneider, B. H. *Feeds of the World: Their Digestibility and Composition.* Morgantown: West Virginia Agricultural Experiment Station, 1947. 299 p.

42.   Scott, H. H. *A History of Tropical Medicine.* Baltimore: Williams & Wilkins, 1939. 2 v.

43.   Sidky, A. R. *The Holstein-Friesian in Egypt: 1. Ten Years Breeding and Crossing Experiment.* Cairo: Government Press, 1939. 15 p.

44. Staley, E. *The Future of Underdeveloped Countries.* New York: Harper, 1954. 410 p.

45a. Stamp, L. D. *Africa: A Study in Tropical Development.* New York: Wiley, 1953. 568 p.

b. —————————. *Land for Tomorrow: The Underdeveloped World.* Bloomington: Indiana University Press, 1952. 230 p.

46. Thirumalai, S. *Post-war Agricultural Problems and Policies in India.* New York: Institute of Pacific Relations, 1954. 280 p.

47a. Thornthwaite, C. W. "An Approach toward a Rational Classification of Climate," *Geographical Review,* v. 38 (1948), pp. 55-94.

b. —————————. "Problems in the Classification of Climates," *Geographical Review,* v. 33 (1943), pp. 233-55.

48a. United Nations. Dept. of Social Affairs. *Housing in the Tropics.* New York, 1952. 148 p. (1952.IV.2.)

b. —————————. —————————. *Preliminary Report on the World Social Situation with Special Reference to Standards of Living.* New York, 1952. 180 p. (1952.-IV.11.)

c. —————————. Statistical Office. *Statistical Yearbook.* New York. Annual.

d. United Nations Scientific Conference on the Conservation and Utilization of Resources, Lake Success, New York, 1949. *Proceedings:* v. 6, *Land Resources.* New York, 1951. 629 p. (1950.IIB.7.)

49a. United States. Dept. of Agriculture. *Agricultural Statistics, 1953.* Washington: GPO, 1953. 777 p.

b. —————————. —————————. *Yearbook of Agriculture; Climate and Man.* Washington: GPO, 1941. 1,248 p.

c. —————————. —————————. *Yearbook of Agriculture; Water.* Washington: GPO, 1955. 751 p.

50. —————————. Housing and Home Finance Agency. *Application of Climatic Data to House Design.* Washington: GPO, 1954. 152 p.

51. —————————. National Research Council. *Housing and Building in Hot-humid and Hot-dry Climates.*

Washington: Author, 1953. 177 p. (Building Research
Advisory Board, Conference Report, 5.)

52. Wagley, C. *Amazon Town: A Study of Man in the
Tropics.* New York: Macmillan, 1953. 295 p.

53. Wilson, C. M. *The Tropics: World of Tomorrow.* New
York: Harper, 1951. 270 p.

54. Winslow, C-E. A. and Herrington, L. P. *Temperature
and Human Life.* Princeton: Princeton University
Press, 1949. 272 p.

55. World Health Organization. *The African Mind in
Health and Disease: A Study in Ethnopsychiatry.* New
York: Columbia University Press, 1953. 177 p. (WHO
Monograph Series, 17.)

56. Woytinsky, W. S. and Woytinsky, E. S. *World Population and Production.* New York: Twentieth Century
Fund, 1953. 1,268 p.

57. Wright, N. *Report on the Development of Cattle Breeding and Production in Ceylon.* Colombo: Ceylon Government Press, 1946. 44 p. (Ceylon State Council Ses-
sional Paper, 20.)